HELLO

Congratulations on owning the best KS2 maths guide!

Here are some top tips to help you get the most out of this book.

1 Make sure you have the correct equipment. You will need the usual maths stuff and we also recommend you use a notebook/paper alongside this workbook for more working out if needed. There's some squared paper on pages 172 to 175 that you could use.

2 Remind yourself of the key facts on the pages called 'Key Facts'. They include stuff you probably already know. If not ... you can turn back to these pages for a reminder at any time.

3 Look at the 'Key Words and Phrases' page. These words and phrases can often appear in questions and tell you what to do. The 'Solving Word Problems' page also has other words that give clues on how to solve a problem.

4 On to the main pages ... attempt the check-in ticket and work through the 'Ready' section. Then have a go at the 'Set' and 'Go' questions (no cheating with the answers at the back ... they're for when you've finished).

5 Return to the same double page a couple of days later and check you still remember the maths. Then and only then are you allowed to tick the checklist and rip off the corner of the page*.

*if it's not your book ... check with the owner!

Also included ... a set of flashcards to cut out to help you remember the times-tables (you can always make more)

On each double-page there are three sections for you to work through:

READY? First complete the check-in, then read the key information and work carefully through the examples. Sometimes highlighting is used to give extra guidance and look out for the maths police who are also there to help!

SET? Jump right in and have a go at these questions. They are closely linked to the worked examples. You can check your answers in the back.

GO! Here we go ... some trickier problems, including SATs-style questions. Again, don't forget to check your answers in the back.

Are you ready? Let's do this!

You're almost ready to get started ... but first you must decide where you will work:

Lying on the floor ☒

On a sofa in front of the TV ☒

At a well-lit desk with a proper chair ☑

What does success look like?

Tick the checklist when you've completed each section

Check a few days later ... still confident?

Ace!

Tear off the corner thingy

2

Contents and Checklist

Always check your answers ... page 177 onwards

Make sure you have all the correct equipment

Know the multiplication table facts (cut out the flashcards)

Check you know what the key words and phrases mean

Believe in yourself ♥

It's no good just owning this book ...
use it!

Smashed it! ☐

GETTING LARGER →

0	10	20	30	40	50	60	70	80	90	100
zero	ten	twenty	thirty	forty	fifty	sixty	seventy	eighty	ninety	one hundred
	X	XX	XXX	XL	L	LX	LXX	LXXX	XC	C

Number facts

0	1	2	3	4	5	6	7	8	9	10
zero	one	two	three	four	five	six	seven	eight	nine	ten
	I	II	III	IV	V	VI	VII	VIII	IX	X

Even numbers can be divided exactly by 2

Numbers can also be written using Roman numerals

Compare and order

Less	←→	More
Minimum	←→	Maximum
Shortest	←→	Longest
Lightest	←→	Heaviest
Smallest	←→	Largest

Smashed it! ☐

Hundreds	Tens	Ones	•	Tenths	Hundredths
4	5	6			

Four hundred and fifty-six

Place value

0 • 4
Zero point four (four tenths)

0 • 0 7
Zero point zero seven (seven hundredths)

Smashed it! ☐

+	0	1	2	3	4	5	6	7	8	9	10
0	0+0=0	1+0=1	2+0=2	3+0=3	4+0=4	5+0=5	6+0=6	7+0=7	8+0=8	9+0=9	10+0=10
1	0+1=1	1+1=2	2+1=3	3+1=4	4+1=5	5+1=6	6+1=7	7+1=8	8+1=9	9+1=10	
2	0+2=2	1+2=3	2+2=4	3+2=5	4+2=6	5+2=7	6+2=8	7+2=9	8+2=10		
3	0+3=3	1+3=4	2+3=5	3+3=6	4+3=7	5+3=8	6+3=9	7+3=10			
4	0+4=4	1+4=5	2+4=6	3+4=7	4+4=8	5+4=9	6+4=10				
5	0+5=5	1+5=6	2+5=7	3+5=8	4+5=9	5+5=10				10+1=11	1
6	0+6=6	1+6=7	2+6=8	3+6=9	4+6=10				9+2=11	10+2=12	2
7	0+7=7	1+7=8	2+7=9	3+7=10				8+3=11	9+3=12	10+3=13	3
8	0+8=8	1+8=9	2+8=10				7+4=11	8+4=12	9+4=13	10+4=14	4
9	0+9=9	1+9=10				6+5=11	7+5=12	8+5=13	9+5=14	10+5=15	5
10	0+10=10				5+6=11	6+6=12	7+6=13	8+6=14	9+6=15	10+6=16	6
				4+7=11	5+7=12	6+7=13	7+7=14	8+7=15	9+7=16	10+7=17	7
			3+8=11	4+8=12	5+8=13	6+8=14	7+8=15	8+8=16	9+8=17	10+8=18	8
		2+9=11	3+9=12	4+9=13	5+9=14	6+9=15	7+9=16	8+9=17	9+9=18	10+9=19	9
	1+10=11	2+10=12	3+10=13	4+10=14	5+10=15	6+10=16	7+10=17	8+10=18	9+10=19	10+10=20	10
	1	2	3	4	5	6	7	8	9	10	+

Addition facts of 10

Adding 0

Doubles

Number bonds

The result of an addition is called a SUM

Smashed it! ☐

Smashed it! ☐

1 × 2 = 2	7 × 2 = 14	1 × 5 = 5	7 × 5 = 35	1 × 10 = 10	7 × 10 = 70
2 × 2 = 4	8 × 2 = 16	2 × 5 = 10	8 × 5 = 40	2 × 10 = 20	8 × 10 = 80
3 × 2 = 6	9 × 2 = 18	3 × 5 = 15	9 × 5 = 45	3 × 10 = 30	9 × 10 = 90
4 × 2 = 8	10 × 2 = 20	4 × 5 = 20	10 × 5 = 50	4 × 10 = 40	10 × 10 = 100
5 × 2 = 10	11 × 2 = 22	5 × 5 = 25	11 × 5 = 55	5 × 10 = 50	11 × 10 = 110
6 × 2 = 12	12 × 2 = 24	6 × 5 = 30	12 × 5 = 60	6 × 10 = 60	12 × 10 = 120

Times tables

The result of a multiplication is called a PRODUCT

Angle and line facts

Right angle exactly 90° | Acute angle less than 90° | Obtuse angle more than 90° and less than 180° | Reflex angle greater than 180°

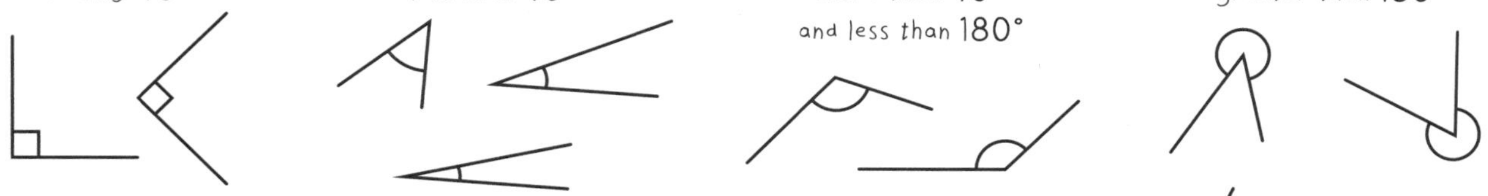

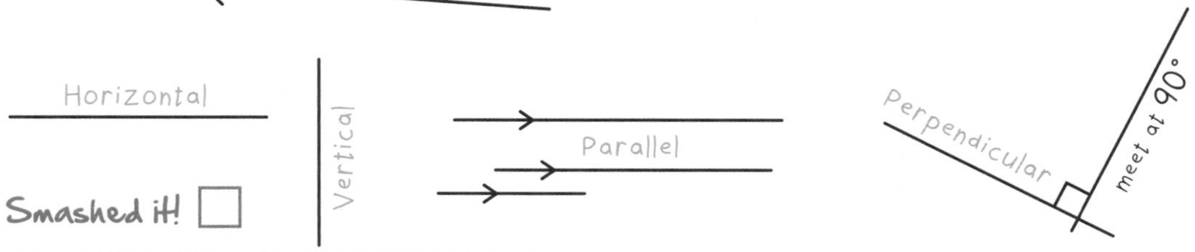
Horizontal
Vertical
Parallel
Perpendicular
meet at 90°

Smashed it! ☐

2D shapes

Name	Number of sides
Triangle	3
Quadrilateral	4
Pentagon	5
Hexagon	6
Heptagon	7
Octagon	8
Nonagon	9
Decagon	10

Polygon
A shape with straight sides

Regular
All sides equal and all angles equal

Smashed it! ☐

Types of triangle

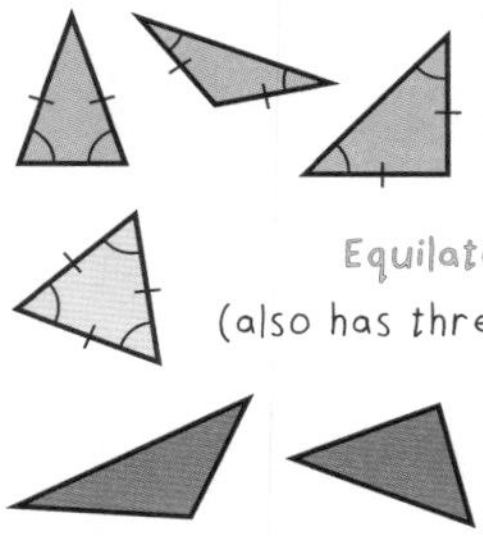

Isosceles: two equal sides (also has two equal angles)

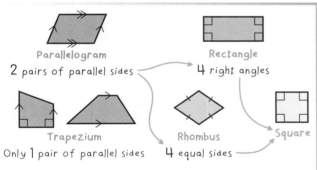

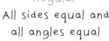

Equilateral: three equal sides (also has three equal angles ... each 60°)

Scalene: no equal sides (and no equal angles)

Any triangle with an angle of 90° is called a right-angled triangle

Smashed it! ☐

3D shapes

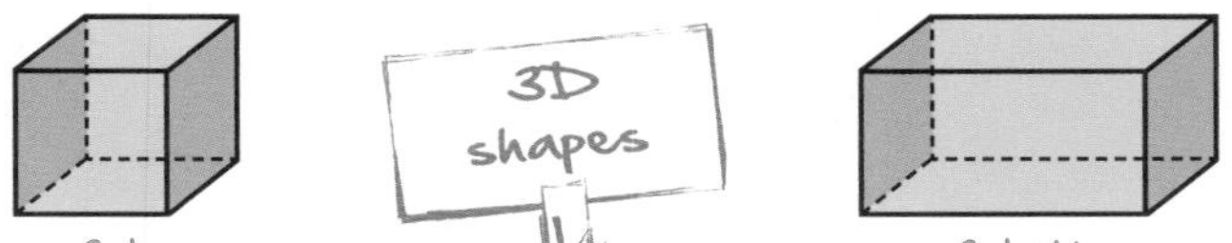
Cube
Cuboid

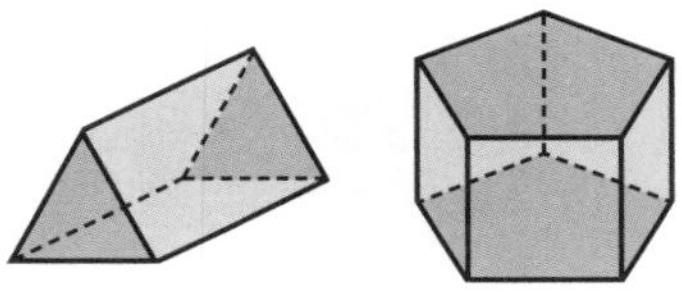

Prism
Same polygon at both ends
Cubes and cuboids are also prisms

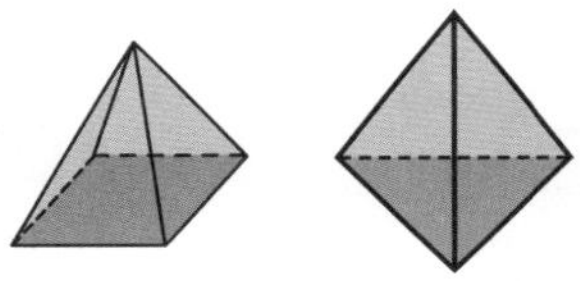

Pyramid
Polygon base and all other faces meeting at a point

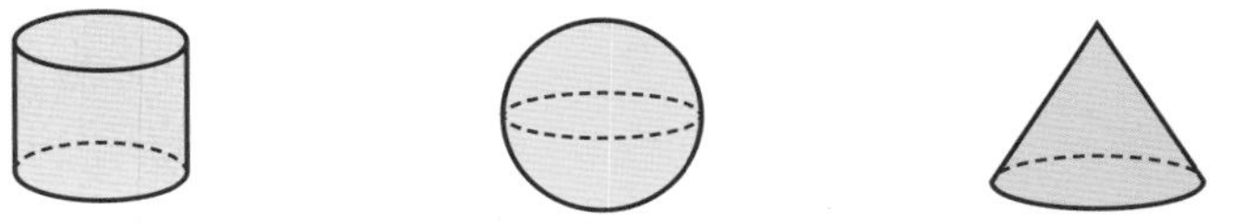
Cylinder
Sphere
Cone

Smashed it! ☐

Types of quadrilateral

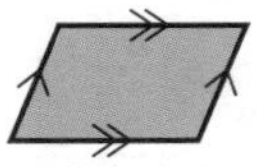

Parallelogram
2 pairs of parallel sides

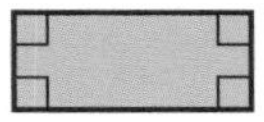

Rectangle
4 right angles

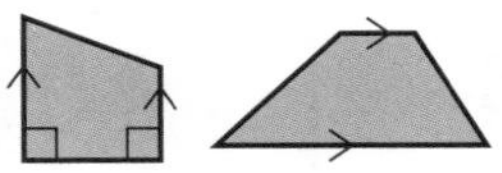

Trapezium
Only 1 pair of parallel sides

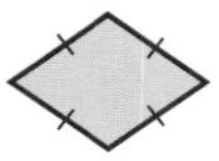

Rhombus
4 equal sides

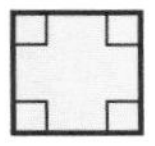

Square

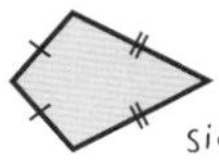

Kite
2 pairs of equal sides next to each other

Smashed it! ☐

Charts and diagrams

Eye Colour	Tally	Frequency
brown	𝍸 I	6
blue	𝍸 III	8
green	III	3
grey	IIII	4
hazel	𝍸	5

Tally chart: a way of collecting data

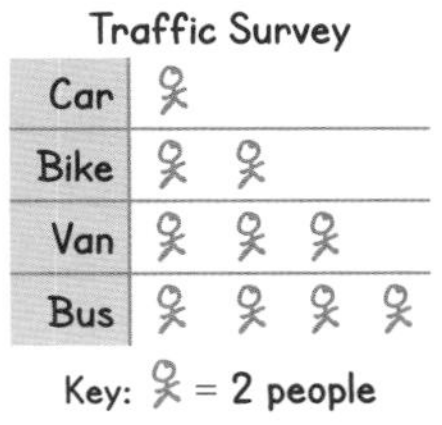
Traffic Survey
Car
Bike
Van
Bus
Key: = 2 people

Pictogram: a way of representing data using symbols

Smashed it! ☐

Time and money

1 minute = 60 seconds
1 hour = 60 minutes
1 day = 24 hours
1 week = 7 days
1 year = 365 days = 12 months

Monday
Tuesday
Wednesday
Thursday
Friday
Saturday
Sunday

January 31 days
February 28 or 29 days
March 31 days
April 30 days
May 31 days
June 30 days

July 31 days
August 31 days
September 30 days
October 31 days
November 30 days
December 31 days

100p = £1
Coins: 1p, 2p, 5p, 10p, 20p, 50p, £1, £2
Notes: £5, £10, £20, £50

Smashed it! ☐

Solving word problems

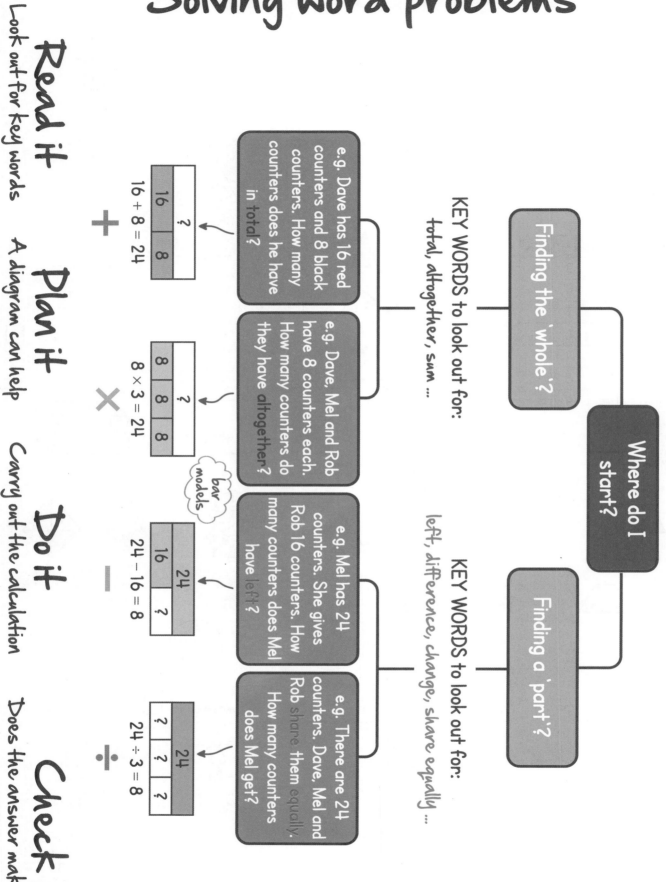

Read it — Look out for key words

Plan it — A diagram can help

Do it — Carry out the calculation

Check it — Does the answer make sense?

Where do I start?

Finding the 'whole'?

KEY WORDS to look out for:
total, altogether, sum ...

e.g. Dave has 16 red counters and 8 black counters. How many counters does he have in total?

16	8
?	

16 + 8 = 24

e.g. Dave, Mel and Rob have 8 counters each. How many counters do they have altogether?

8	8	8
?		

8 × 3 = 24

bar models

Finding a 'part'?

KEY WORDS to look out for:
left, difference, change, share equally ...

e.g. Mel has 24 counters. She gives Rob 16 counters. How many counters does Mel have left?

24	
16	?

24 − 16 = 8

e.g. There are 24 counters. Dave, Mel and Rob share them equally. How many counters does Mel get?

24		
?	?	?

24 ÷ 3 = 8

6

3 × 3	4 × 9	7 × 11
3 × 4	4 × 11	7 × 12
3 × 6	4 × 12	8 × 8
3 × 7	6 × 6	8 × 9
3 × 8	6 × 7	8 × 11
3 × 9	6 × 8	8 × 12
3 × 11	6 × 9	9 × 9
3 × 12	6 × 11	9 × 11
4 × 4	6 × 12	9 × 12
4 × 6	7 × 7	11 × 11
4 × 7	7 × 8	11 × 12

4 × 8	7 × 9	12 × 12

77	36	9
84	44	12
64	48	18
72	36	21
88	42	24
96	48	27
81	54	33
99	66	36
108	72	16
121	49	24
132	56	28
144	63	32

KEY WORDS AND PHRASES

Key words and phrases tell you to 'do something'

ORDER

Use a rule to arrange:

Order from smallest to largest
24, 2, 2.41, 2.7
2, 2.41, 2.7, 24

SIMPLIFY

Make a fraction simpler by cancelling common factors:

$$\frac{12}{16} = \frac{3}{4}$$

CALCULATE

$53 + 41$
$= 94$

HOW MUCH ...?

... change will I get from £5?

Perform one or more steps to get an answer

ROUND

Make a number simpler but keep its value close to what it was:

24.26 rounded to ...
one decimal place is 24.3
the nearest ten is 20

WRITE

Give the answer without needing to show working out:

Write $\frac{3}{4}$ as a decimal
0.75

WORK OUT

8×2
$= 16$

FIND

the next number in the sequence
3, 6, 9, 12, 15

EXPLAIN

Give reasons to support the decision or the answer

ESTIMATE

Give a sensible approximate answer using rounding:

Estimate 49×31
$50 \times 30 = 1500$

MEASURE

Find the length of a line or size of an angle using ...

... a ruler or protractor

GIVE REASONS

Explain your thinking, such as

'because a square has 4 equal sides'

DRAW

Create an accurate drawing of a shape or diagram

COMPLETE

Fill in missing values in a table or add lines on a diagram to complete a shape:

Add 2 lines to make a pentagon

MARK or LABEL

Attach the correct name or position on a number line, such as

Edge

PLOT

Mark a point on a graph using a cross:

Plot the point (1,2)

MATCH

Connect items with the correct value or name:

Square
Pentagon
Triangle

CONVERT

Change from one form to another:

Convert 3 m to centimetres
$3 \times 100 = 300$ cm

SHADE

Add colour to highlight something:

Shade one quarter of the shape

DECREASE

Make an amount smaller:

Decrease 35 by 10
$= 25$

SHOW

Give all workings to get to the answer

INCREASE

Make an amount larger:

Increase 35 by 10
$= 45$

TRUE or FALSE

Is a statement correct or not correct?

READY?

Place value is used to read and write numbers.

Hundred Thousands	Ten Thousands	Thousands	Hundreds	Tens	Ones
●●●●●	●●●	●●	● ● ●	●	●●●

The number represented in the table is 532,413

In the number **532**,413:
* the digit **2** is worth **2 thousands**,
* the digit **3** is worth **3 ten thousands**, and
* the digit **5** is worth **5 hundred thousands**.

It is written in words as: five hundred and thirty-two thousand, four hundred and thirteen.

e.g. 1 Write the number 29,358 using words.

TTh	Th	H	T	O
2	9	3	5	8

Twenty-nine thousand, three hundred and fifty-eight

e.g. 2 Write the number two hundred and thirty-one thousand, six hundred and forty-five in numerals.

HTh	TTh	Th	H	T	O
2	3	1	6	4	5

There are two hundred and thirty-one thousands

Six hundreds, four tens and five ones

231,645

We can use place value to find the value of any digits.

e.g. 3 Here is a number: 239,860

a) Write down the value of the digit 3

HTh	TTh	Th	H	T	O
2	3	9	8	6	0

The digit 3 is worth 3 ten thousands (or 30,000)

b) Write down the value of the digit 2

The digit 2 is worth 2 hundred thousands (or 200,000)

We can easily find 1,000 more or less than a number ...

e.g. 4 Find one thousand more than 47,208

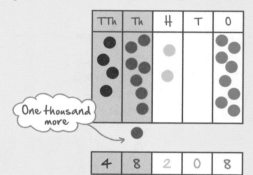

One thousand more

4	8	2	0	8

One thousand more than 47,208 is 48,208

The thousands column has increased by 1 ... the other columns have all stayed the same

---

SET?

A. Write down the value of the 8 in each number:

(i) 82,615

(ii) 70,832

(iii) 38,006

(iv) 801,652

B. Write the numbers using numerals:

(i) Sixty-seven thousand, four hundred and twenty-three

(ii) Six thousand and sixty-two

(iii) Eight hundred thousand and eighty

C. Write the numbers in words:

(i) 54,417

(ii) 62,091

(iii) 140,307

D. Find ten thousand more than 31,709

E. Find one thousand less than two hundred and ninety-three thousand, two hundred.

Write your answer using numerals.

Excellent!

1. Complete the table.

1,000 less	Number	1,000 more
	38,734	
	310,627	
9,070		

2. Rocco writes the number one hundred and thirty-six thousand and seventy as:

136000,70

Rocco is not correct.

Describe the mistake that he has made.

3. Simeon is running the London Marathon.

It is approximately 42,000 metres long.

He has completed thirty thousand metres.

How much further does he need to run?

m

4. Here are some clues for a mystery number:

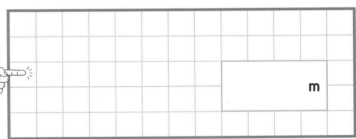

It is a 5-digit number

It is odd

It contains two zeros

It is divisible by 5

It is greater than 30,000

It includes the digits 2 and 4

Find all the possible values for the number.

5. Estimate the value of the numbers at the positions labelled A, B and C.

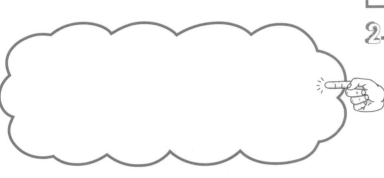

A

B

C

READY?

Place value is also used to read and write larger numbers.

Millions	Hundred Thousands	Ten Thousands	Thousands	Hundreds	Tens	Ones

The number represented in the table is 3,216,450

In the number **3,216**,450:

* the digit **6** is worth **6 thousands,**
* the digit **1** is worth **1 ten thousand,**
* the digit **2** is worth **2 hundred thousands,** and
* the digit **3** is worth **3 millions.**

It is written in words as: three million, two hundred and sixteen thousand, four hundred and fifty.

e.g. 1   a) Write the number 8,561,324 using words.

M	HTh	TTh	Th	H	T	O
8	5	6	1	3	2	4

Eight million, five hundred and sixty-one thousand, three hundred and twenty-four

b) What is the value of the digit 6 in the number 8,561,324?

The digit 6 is worth 6 ten thousands
(or 60,000)

The 6 is NOT worth 60

CHECK-IN
JUSTAROO Airlines

1. Write 40,526 in words
2. Write three hundred and ten thousand, five hundred and seventy-eight using numerals
3. Circle the value of the underlined digit in the number 4<u>2</u>1,300:
      2   20   2,000   20,000

Ready for take off?

We can use place value to write numbers given in words as numerals.

e.g. 2   Write the number two million, one hundred and eighty-five thousand and forty-three in numerals.

There are two millions

There are one hundred and eighty-five thousands

M	HTh	TTh	Th	H	T	O
2	1	8	5	0	4	3

Four tens and three ones

2,185,043

We can easily find 1 million more or less than a number ...

e.g. 3   Find one million more than 4,325,602

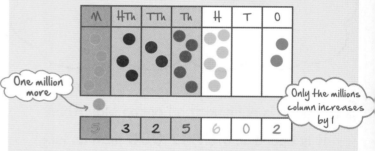

One million more

M	HTh	TTh	Th	H	T	O
5	3	2	5	6	0	2

Only the millions column increases by 1

One million more than 4,325,602 is 5,325,602

One million has six zeros ... 1,000,000

SET?

A. Write down the value of the 6 in each number:

(i) 6,382,905

(ii) 3,620,541

(iii) 462,703

B. Write the numbers using numerals:

(i) Five million

(ii) Five million, three hundred and fifty-seven thousand, two hundred and sixty-one

(iii) Five million and fifty-three thousand

C. Write the numbers in words:

(i) 1,246,783

(ii) 3,726,070

(iii) 401,896

(iv) 10,000,000

D. Find one million more than 5,237,601

E. Find one million less than six million, one hundred and twenty-three thousand, five hundred.

Write your answer using numerals.

Result!

1. Write the number one less than one million in words.

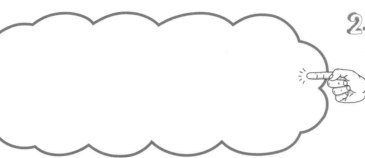

2. Angela writes the number six million, six hundred thousand, and sixty-six as:

   6,600,66

   Do you agree with Angela? Explain your answer.

3. Write numbers in the empty boxes so that each number can be matched with its description in words.

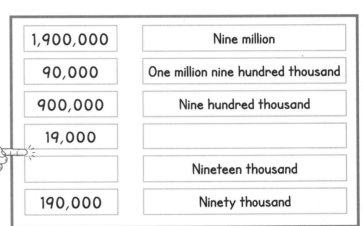

1,900,000	Nine million
90,000	One million nine hundred thousand
900,000	Nine hundred thousand
19,000	
	Nineteen thousand
190,000	Ninety thousand

4. A music video has 1,250,000 views in its first week.

   In the second week there are 400,000 fewer views.

   How many views are there in the second week?

5. Estimate the value of the numbers at the positions labelled A, B and C.

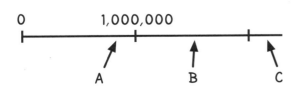

A

B

C

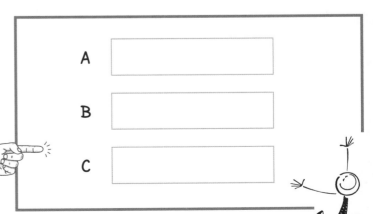

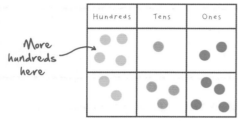

READY?

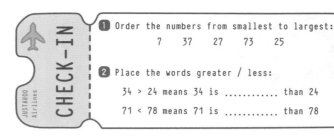

CHECK-IN

JUSTAROO Airlines

1. Order the numbers from smallest to largest:
   7   37   27   73   25

2. Place the words greater / less:
   34 > 24 means 34 is .... than 24
   71 < 78 means 71 is .... than 78

Ready for take off?

Place value can also be used to compare and order numbers. For example, 412 is greater than 234 because it has more hundreds.

Hundreds	Tens	Ones

More hundreds here

412 > 234

e.g. 1 Use <, = or > to complete the statement:

456 ◯ 812

1. Consider the digits with the highest place value (a table could help)
   456   812

H	T	O
4	5	6
8	1	2

2. Compare ... 4 hundreds is less than 8 hundreds

456 < 812

e.g. 2 Use <, = or > to complete the statement:

324 ◯ 87

The table is really useful when there are a different number of digits

H	T	O
3	2	4
	8	7

87 has zero hundreds

8 > 3, but this does NOT make 87 greater than 324

324 > 87

e.g. 3 Put a ring around the smallest number:

786   782   728   768

H	T	O
7	8	6
7	8	2
7	2	8
7	6	8

All of the numbers are 'seven hundred and something', so ...

728 has the smallest number of tens

... compare the number of tens

786   782   (728)   768

e.g. 4 Order the numbers from smallest to largest:

725   527   723   372

1. Compare the number of hundreds:
   725   527   723   372

H	T	O
7	2	5
5	2	7
7	2	3
3	7	2

2. Order by the number of hundreds:
   372   527   725   723

3. Compare the number of tens:
   725   723

4. Compare the number of ones:
   725   723

5 > 3 so 725 > 723

5. Write all of the numbers in order:
   372   527   723   725

A. Use <, = or > to complete the statement:

(i)   425 ◯ 638

(ii)   568 ◯ 312

(iii) 290 ◯ 902

(iv)   124 ◯ 63

(v)   94 ◯ 409

B. Use <, = or > to complete the statement:

(i)   325 ◯ 318

(ii)   990 ◯ 902

(iii) 127 ◯ 123

(iv)   494 ◯ 490

C. Circle the smallest number:

(i)   456   654   546   765

(ii)   312   213   132   413

(iii) 789   98   978   879

(iv)   240   204   402   420

(v)   789   784   798   794

D. Order the numbers from smallest to largest:

(i)   872   478   278   724

(ii)   543   54   540   547

(iii) 807   99   909   990

COMPARING AND ORDERING 1

1. Use the digits 7, 8 and 9 to create four different three-digit numbers.

Write your numbers in order from largest to smallest.

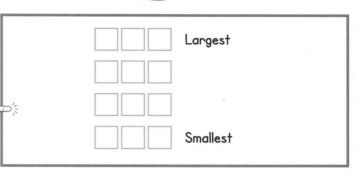

Largest

Smallest

2. Roberto is given these numbers:

105   314   278

He says:

"278 is the largest number because it includes 8, which is the largest digit of them all"

Do you agree with Roberto? Explain why.

3. Always true / Sometimes true / Never true:

A three-digit number that includes a digit 9 is greater than a three-digit number that does not include a digit 9

Explain your answer.

4. Match the numbers with the correct position.

678	1st	Largest
87	2nd	
687	3rd	
786	4th	
768	5th	Smallest

5. Four numbers are written in order. Find the missing digits.

2 8 ☐   Smallest

2 ☐ 1

☐ 8 5

2 ☐ 1   Largest

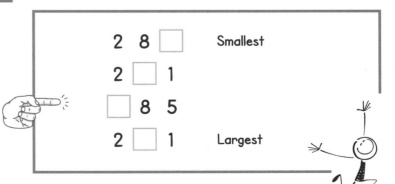

Place value can be used to compare and order larger numbers too. For example, 230,134 is greater than 143,401 because it has more **hundred thousands**.

Hundred Thousands	Ten Thousands	Thousands	Hundreds	Tens	Ones
● ●	● ● ●		●	● ● ●	● ● ● ●
● ●	● ● ● ●	● ● ●	● ● ●		●

230,134 > 143,401

✈ CHECK-IN JUSTAROO Airlines

1 Order the numbers from smallest to largest:
   81   880   801   180   810

2 Place the words greater / less:
   429 < 452 means 429 is .... than 452
   601 > 298 means 601 is .... than 298

Ready for take off?

e.g. 1 Use <, = or > to complete the statement:

45,627 ◯ 81,253

1 Consider the digits with the highest place value

TTh	Th	H	T	O
4	5	6	2	7
8	1	2	5	3

2 Compare ... 4 ten thousands is less than 8 ten thousands

45,627 < 81,253

e.g. 2 Use <, = or > to complete the statement:

132,405 ◯ 98,769

HTh	TTh	Th	H	T	O
1	3	2	4	0	5
	9	8	7	6	9

98,769 has no hundred thousands

132,405 > 98,769

e.g. 3 Put a ring around the largest number:

564,136   581,049   529,874   546,213

1 Compare the number of hundred thousands: all of the numbers have five hundred thousands

HTh	TTh	Th	H	T	O
5	6	4	1	3	6
5	8	1	0	4	9
5	2	9	8	7	4
5	4	6	2	1	3

2 Compare the number of ten thousands

564,136   (581,049)   529,874   546,213

We can also use place value to order numbers.

e.g. 4 Order the numbers from smallest to largest:

87,506   72,834   87,256   9,543

1 Compare and order by the number of ten thousands:

2 These two are the same ... now compare the number of thousands

No change

TTh	Th	H	T	O
	9	5	4	3
7	2	8	3	4
8	7	5	0	6
8	7	2	5	6

3 So now compare and order by the number of hundreds

8	7	2	5	6
8	7	5	0	6

4 Write the numbers in order

9,543   72,834   87,256   87,506

A. Use <, = or > to complete the statement:

(i) 42,516 ◯ 63,827

(ii) 56,803 ◯ 31,296

(iii) 129,018 ◯ 392,801

(iv) 312,456 ◯ 400,890

(v) 9,401 ◯ 4,109

C. Put a ring around the largest number:

(i) 45,263   65,432   42,536   56,237

(ii) 635,823   253,798   442,987   153,897

(iii) 95,802   9,897   91,654   94,237

B. Use <, = or > to complete the statement:

(i) 42,281 ◯ 41,506

(ii) 256,832 ◯ 275,124

(iii) 98,756 ◯ 98,657

(iv) 102,706 ◯ 12,762

D. Order the numbers from smallest to largest:

(i) 53,237   25,263   35,432   52,536

(ii) 145,802   76,897   351,654   242,237

(iii) 30,503   30,500   30,530   35,000

(iv) 10,702   9,256   10,072   9,265

 **GO!**

1. Use the digits 0, 1, 2, 3, 4 and 5 once each to complete the statements.

☐2,654 < 2☐,456

5☐,807 > 5☐,708

☐,312 < ☐9,213

2. Here are the heights of some mountains:

Everest	29,029 metres
K7	22,749 metres
Matterhorn	14,692 metres
K12	24,370 metres
K2	28,251 metres

Some of the mountains have a 'K number'. Matt thinks that the larger the K number, the taller the mountain.

Do you agree? Explain why.

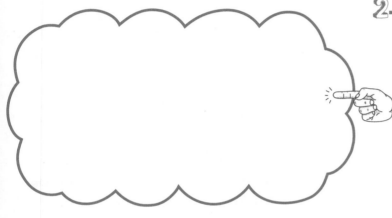

3. Tick all the numbers that are greater than four hundred thousand.

7,100 ☐

450,000 ☐

910,500 ☐

Half a million ☐

55,500 ☐

4. Four numbers are written in order.

All the missing digits are different.

Find the missing digits.

132,7☐6   Smallest

13☐,781

132,85☐

1☐2,857   Largest

READY?

A place value chart is still helpful when comparing and ordering larger numbers ... 3,214,103 is greater than 1,427,325 because it has more **millions**.

Millions	Hundred Thousands	Ten Thousands	Thousands	Hundreds	Tens	Ones
○○○	●● ●	● ●	●● ●●●	●		●● ●
○○○	●● ●	● ●	●● ● ●●●	● ●	●	●● ●

3,214,103 > 1,427,325

e.g. 1   Use <, = or > to complete the statement:

5,213,253 ◯ 4,645,328

1 Consider the digits with the highest place

M	HTh	TTh	Th	H	T	O
5	2	1	3	2	5	3
4	6	4	5	3	2	8

2 Compare ... 5 millions is more than 4 millions

5,213,253 (>) 4,645,328

e.g. 2   Use <, = or > to complete the statement:

985,667 ◯ 1,320,405

M	HTh	TTh	Th	H	T	O
	9	8	5	6	6	7
1	3	2	0	4	0	5

985,667 has no millions

Do NOT compare the 9 and the 1

985,667 (<) 1,320,405

e.g. 3   Put a ring around the largest number:

4,156,413   4,258,986   4,302,104   4,194,621

1 Compare the number of millions ... all of the numbers have **four** millions

M	HTh	TTh	Th	H	T	O
4	1	5	6	4	1	3
4	2	5	8	9	8	6
4	3	0	2	1	0	4
4	1	9	4	6	2	1

2 Compare the number of **hundred thousands**

4,156,413   4,258,986   (4,302,104)   4,194,621

We can also use place value to order numbers.

e.g. 4   Order the numbers from smallest to largest:

3,681,506   2,052,834   3,186,253   960,543

1 Compare and order by the number of millions:

M	HTh	TTh	Th	H	T	O
	9	6	0	5	4	3
2	0	5	2	8	3	4
3	6	8	1	5	0	6
3	1	8	6	2	5	3

2 Compare and order the number of **hundred thousands**

3	1	8	6	2	5	3
3	6	8	1	5	0	6

1 < 6 so 3,186,253 < 3,681,506

3 Write the numbers in order

960,543   2,052,834   3,186,253   3,681,506

SET?

A. Use <, = or > to complete the statement:

(i) 1,642,516 ◯ 3,763,827

(ii) 4,156,803 ◯ 3,931,296

(iii) 7,004,018 ◯ 9,002,001

(iv) 987,654 ◯ 3,210,123

(v) 708,497 ◯ 1 million

B. Use <, = or > to complete the statement:

(i) 2,142,281 ◯ 2,741,506

(ii) 3,908,756 ◯ 3,098,657

(iii) 457,206 ◯ 4,572,060

(iv) 3 million ◯ 3,000,000

C. Put a ring around the largest number:

(i) 2,035,823   3,350,798   2,420,987   1,042,897

(ii) 9,465,802   987,654   9,521,654   9,004,237

(iii) 2,040,000   2,004,400   2,004,200   2,400,002

(iv) 3,125,802   4 million   1,304,207   456,789

D. Order the numbers from smallest to largest:

(i) 2,345,263   3,456,432   4,765,536   3,876,237

(ii) 2,127,823   3,106,798   2,516,987   4,615,897

(iii) 2,030,503   230,500   2,003,530   2,300,050

18

GO!

COMPARING AND ORDERING 3

1. Use the digits 3, 4, 5 and 6 to complete the statement.

Write down all the possible different solutions.

3,☐6☐,500 > ☐,☐80,500

2. Tracey is given these numbers:

1,304,567   986,879   5,746,012

She says:

"986,879 is the largest number because it's the only one that starts with a 9"

Explain why Tracey is not correct.

3. Here are the populations of some countries:

Luxembourg	626,108
Switzerland	8,655,100
Denmark	5,837,213
Bulgaria	6,951,482
Malta	514,564

Donny thinks that all the countries have a population greater than five million.

Do you agree with Donny? Explain your answer.

4. Match the numbers with the correct position.

| Half a million |
| 4,500,000 |
| 487,700 |
| 2 million |
| 4,000,500 |

1st	Largest
2nd	
3rd	
4th	
5th	Smallest

READY?

Rounding is used to estimate the value of numbers, such as when checking if the answer to a calculation is sensible. We can round in different ways:

164 rounded to the nearest 10 is 160

164

164 rounded to the nearest 100 is 200

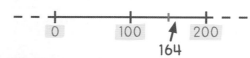

164

e.g. 1   Round 32 to the nearest 10

1 On a number line, mark the multiples of 10 that are closest to 32

32

2 Position 32 on the number line

3 Use the halfway point to decide if it's closer to 30 or 40

32 rounded to the nearest 10 is 30

e.g. 2   Round 265 to the nearest 10

1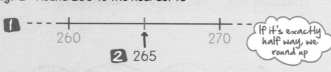

260   265   270

If it's exactly half way, we round up

2 265

3 265 rounded to the nearest 10 is 270

CHECK-IN

JUSTAROO Airlines

1 Put a ring around all the multiples of 10:
5   40   75   120   155

2 Put a ring around all the multiples of 100:
1   100   250   460   1,000

3 Find the number exactly halfway between:
a) 40 and 50   b) 600 and 700

Ready for take off?

e.g. 3   Round 278 to the nearest 100

1 Mark the multiples of 100 that are closest to 278

200   300

2 278

3 278 rounded to the nearest 100 is 300

We can use place value to round numbers without drawing number lines ...

e.g. 4   a) Round 425 to the nearest 10

1 Draw a 'chop line' between the tens and ones   42|5   **2** Check the digit to the right of the chop line

3 If this digit is 4 or less, the tens digit is not changed
If this digit is 5 or above, the tens digit increases by 1

4 The answer is a multiple of 10 ... write a zero as a placeholder here   43|0

425 rounded to the nearest 10 is 430

b) Round 425 to the nearest 100

1 'Chop' between hundreds and tens   4|25   **2** Look to the right of the chop line

3 This digit is 2, so the hundreds digit is not changed

4 Use zeros as placeholders   4|00

425 rounded to the nearest 100 is 400

A. Round to the nearest 10:
(i)   52
(ii) 87
(iii) 167
(iv) 402
(v)   798

B. Round to the nearest 10:
(i)   135
(ii) 555
(iii) 705
(iv) 295

C. Round to the nearest 100:
(i)   237
(ii) 485
(iii) 167
(iv) 751
(v)   960

D. Round to the nearest 100:
(i)   250
(ii) 450
(iii) 905
(iv) 950

SET?

E. Tick all the options that have an answer of 400:

362 rounded to the nearest 10   ☐

435 rounded to the nearest 100   ☐

394 rounded to the nearest 10   ☐

350 rounded to the nearest 100   ☐

405 rounded to the nearest 100   ☐

404 rounded to the nearest 10   ☐

ROUNDING 1

1. What is the smallest number that can be rounded to 500 when:

a) rounding to the nearest 100?

b) rounding to the nearest 10?

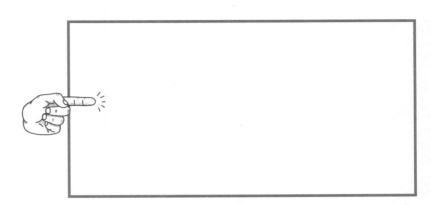

2. Carlos is rounding numbers to the nearest 10. He writes:

365 rounded to the nearest 10 is 360

Explain the mistake that Carlos has made.

3. There are some sweets in a jar.

Bethia says,
"There are 600 sweets to the nearest 10"

Jade says,
"There are 600 sweets to the nearest 100"

Explain why they could both be correct.

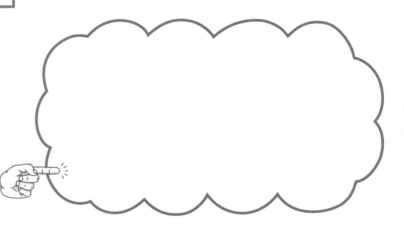

4. Use the digits 9, 7, 6, 5 and 0 once each to complete the statement.

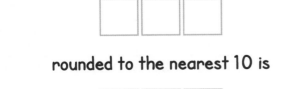

rounded to the nearest 10 is

 0

READY?

As numbers become larger, there are even more ways to round them. For example, to the nearest 1,000 or 10,000 …

28,374 rounded to the **nearest 1,000** is 28,000

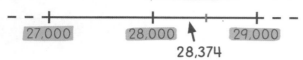

```
- - +----------+----------+----------+ - -
    27,000     28,000  ↑  29,000
               28,374
```

28,374 rounded to the **nearest 10,000** is 30,000

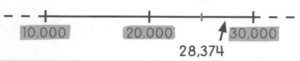

```
- - +----------+----------+----------+ - -
   10,000     20,000   ↑ 30,000
              28,374
```

e.g. 1   Round 4,137 to the nearest 1,000

1 Write down the multiples of 1,000 that are closest to 4,137

```
- - - +----------+----------+ - - -
     4,000  ↗        5,000
          4,137
```

2 Position 4,137 on the number line

3 Use the halfway point to decide if it's closer to 4,000 or 5,000

4,137 rounded to the nearest 1,000 is 4,000

e.g. 2   Round 56,738 to the nearest 1,000

1
```
- - - +----------+----------+ - - -
    56,000      ↑    57,000
        2   56,738
```

3 56,738 rounded to the nearest 1,000 is 57,000

CHECK-IN   JUSTAROO Airlines

1 Circle the multiples of 10,000:

20,000   35,000   61,000   100,000   150,000

2 What number is exactly halfway between 7,000 and 8,000?

3 235 rounded to the nearest 100 is:

200   300   250   2

Ready for take off?

e.g. 3   Round 56,738 to the nearest 10,000

1 Mark the multiples of 10,000 that are closest to 56,738

```
- - - +----------+----↑-----+ - - -
     50,000         60,000
            2  56,738
```

3 56,738 rounded to the nearest 10,000 is 60,000

We can round numbers without drawing number lines by using place value …

e.g. 4   a) Round 83,500 to the nearest 1,000

1 Draw a 'chop line' between the thousands and hundreds   83|500   **2** Check the digit to the right of the chop line

3 If this digit is 4 or less, the thousands digit is not changed
If this digit is 5 or above, the thousands digit increases by 1

4 The answer is a multiple of 1,000 … write zeros as placeholders here   84|000

83,500 rounded to the nearest 1,000 is 84,000

b) Round 83,500 to the nearest 10,000

1 'Chop' between ten thousands and thousands   8|3,500   **2** Check here

3 This digit is 3, so no change

4 Use zeros as placeholders   8|0,000

83,500 rounded to the nearest 10,000 is 80,000

SET

A. Round to the nearest 1,000:
(i)   3,452
(ii) 6,814
(iii) 7,630
(iv) 1,304
(v)   9,500

B. Round to the nearest 1,000:
(i)   13,452
(ii) 26,814
(iii) 47,530
(iv) 99,500

C. Round to the nearest 10,000:
(i)   13,452
(ii) 26,814
(iii) 47,530
(iv) 81,304
(v)   99,500

D. Round to the nearest 10,000:
(i)   25,432
(ii) 35,000
(iii) 54,050
(iv) 34,999

E. Match the numbers with the correct rounding:

15,675 to the nearest 1,000	15,680
15,675 to the nearest 10	22,000
18,500 to the nearest 10,000	19,000
20,950 to the nearest 100	16,000
21,500 to the nearest 1,000	21,000
15,675 to the nearest 100	20,000
18,500 to the nearest 1,000	15,700

GO!

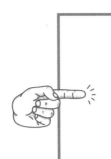

ROUNDING 2

1. What is the smallest number that can be rounded to 50,000 when:

a) rounding to the nearest 100?

b) rounding to the nearest 1,000?

c) rounding to the nearest 10,000?

2. Betty is rounding numbers to the nearest 10,000. She writes:

36,750 rounded to the nearest 10,000 is 37,000

Explain the mistake that Betty has made.

3. The population of Justown is 63,000 when rounded to the nearest 1,000

The population of Kanity is 60,000 when rounded to the nearest 10,000

Explain how the population of Kanity could be greater than the population of Justown.

4. Always true / Sometimes true / Never true:

A four-digit number rounded to the nearest 1,000 is a four-digit number

Explain your answer.

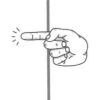

READY?

Using a number line can still be helpful when rounding even larger numbers ...

328,374 rounded to the **nearest 10,000** is 330,000

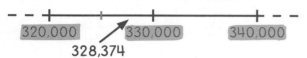

328,374

328,374 rounded to the nearest **100,000** is 300,000

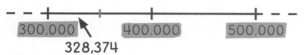

328,374

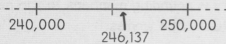

e.g. 1 Round 246,137 to the nearest 10,000

1 Write down the multiples of 10,000 that are closest to 246,137

240,000   250,000

246,137

2 Position 246,137 on the number line   **3** Use the halfway point to decide if it's closer to 240,000 or 250,000

246,137 rounded to the nearest 10,000 is 250,000

e.g. 2 Round 246,137 to the nearest 100,000

1 200,000   300,000

2 246,137

3 246,137 rounded to the nearest 100,000 is 200,000

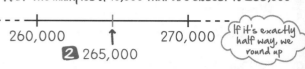
e.g. 3 Round 265,000 to the nearest 10,000

1 Mark the multiples of 10,000 that are closest to 265,000

260,000   270,000

2 265,000

If it's exactly half way, we round up

3 265,000 rounded to the nearest 10,000 is 270,000

We can use place value ...

e.g. 4 a) Round 483,726 to the nearest 10,000

1 Draw the 'chop line' between the ten thousands and thousands   48**3**,726   **2** Check the digit to the right

3 If this digit is 5 or above, the ten thousands digit increases by 1. Otherwise ... no change!

4 The answer is a multiple of 10,000 ... write zeros as placeholders here   48**0**,000

483,726 rounded to the nearest 10,000 is 480,000

b) Round 483,726 to the nearest 100,000

1 'Chop line' here   4**8**3,726   **2** Check this digit

3 This digit is above 5, so we round up

4 Fill in the zeros   5**00**,000

483,726 rounded to the nearest 100,000 is 500,000

SET?

A. Round to the nearest 10,000:

(i) 132,451

(ii) 268,714

(iii) 376,230

(iv) 506,304

(v) 489,300

B. Round to the nearest 10,000:

(i) 135,451

(ii) 255,714

(iii) 374,530

(iv) 500,500

(v) 495,300

C. Round each number to the nearest 100,000:

(i) 135,451   (iv) 590,599

(ii) 275,714   (v) 895,300

(iii) 305,930   (vi) 53,973

D. Round to the nearest 100,000:

(i) 150,451

(ii) 245,714

(iii) 350,930

(iv) 599,599

(v) 999,000

ROUNDING 3

1. Tick all the options with half a million as the answer.

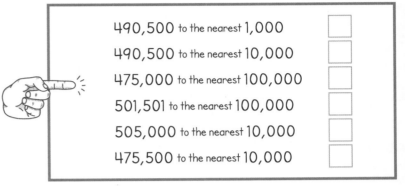

490,500 to the nearest 1,000 ☐

490,500 to the nearest 10,000 ☐

475,000 to the nearest 100,000 ☐

501,501 to the nearest 100,000 ☐

505,000 to the nearest 10,000 ☐

475,500 to the nearest 10,000 ☐

2. Hannah is rounding numbers to the nearest 100,000. She writes:

Quarter of one million rounded to the nearest 100,000 is 200,000

Explain why Hannah is not correct.

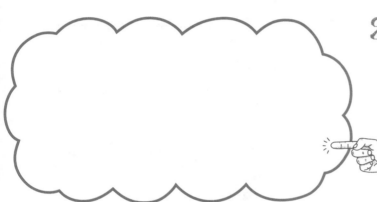

3. Here are some numbers:

157,000   149,000   154,000

Place the numbers in the correct position in the diagram.

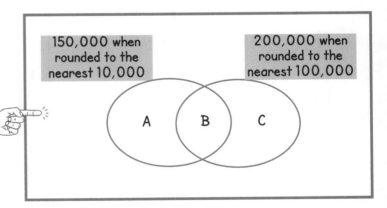

150,000 when rounded to the nearest 10,000

200,000 when rounded to the nearest 100,000

A   B   C

4. Eve has won some money.

The amount of money rounded to the nearest £10,000 is £100,000

What is the largest amount of money she could have won?

£

READY?

There are other ways to round numbers, such as to the nearest whole number or to the nearest tenth.

6.28 rounded to the nearest whole number is 6

6.28 rounded to the nearest tenth is 6.3

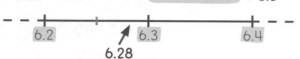

Rounding to the nearest tenth is more commonly known as rounding to one decimal place (1 d.p.)

e.g. 1 Round 5.2 to the nearest whole number

1 Write down the whole numbers that are closest to 5.2

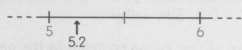

2 Position 5.2 on the number line

3 Decide if it's closer to 5 or 6 by thinking about the halfway point
5.2 rounded to the nearest whole number is 5

e.g. 2 Round 3.84 to the nearest whole number

1
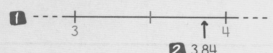

2 3.84

3 3.84 rounded to the nearest whole number is 4

CHECK-IN

JUSTAROO Airlines

Ready for take off?

1 Order the numbers from smallest to largest:

1.4   1.42   1.3   1.35   1.04

2 What number is exactly halfway between 7 and 8?

3 What number is exactly halfway between 6.3 and 6.4?

e.g. 3 Round 3.84 to one decimal place

1 Mark the multiples of tenths that are closest to 3.84

2 3.84

3 3.84 rounded to 1 d.p. is 3.8

Using place value ...

e.g. 4 a) Round 4.25 to the nearest whole number

1 Draw the 'chop line' between the ones and tenths   4|25   2 Check the digit to the right

3 If this digit is 5 or above, the ones digit is increased by 1. Otherwise ... no change!

4 Write the answer as a whole number

4.25 rounded to the nearest whole number is 4

b) Round 4.25 to one decimal place

1 The 'chop line' goes between tenths and hundredths   4.2|5   2 Check the digit to the right

3 This digit is 5, so we round up

4 Write the answer as a number with one decimal place

4.25 rounded to 1 d.p. is 4.3

SET?

A. Round to the nearest whole number:

(i) 6.2

(ii) 2.6

(iii) 9.3

(iv) 3.9

(v) 12.7

C. Round to one decimal place:

(i) 6.51

(ii) 16.57

(iii) 9.38

(iv) 43.06

(v) 0.79

(vi) 0.12

B. Round to the nearest whole number:

(i) 6.5

(ii) 16.57

(iii) 9.35

(iv) 43.25

(v) 12.79

D. Round to one decimal place:

(i) 6.15

(ii) 16.75

(iii) 0.35

(iv) 43.56

(v) 0.75

1. Pat is shopping.

She buys some fruit for £1.78, 85p, £3.07, £2.80 and 99p

She estimates she has spent around £10

How could she have reached this conclusion?

HINT: Rounding is used to estimate

2. Anneka is rounding numbers to the nearest whole number. She writes:

0.9 rounded to the nearest whole number is 0

Explain why Anneka is not correct.

3. Chris takes part in a 100 metre running race.

His time is 12 seconds when rounded to the nearest whole number.

What is the quickest time in which he could have run the race?

seconds

☐.☐☐ to the nearest whole number is ☐

☐.☐☐ to the nearest whole number is ☐

☐.☐☐ to the nearest whole number is ☐

☐.☐☐ to the nearest whole number is ☐

4. Use the digits 5, 6, 7 and 8 to complete this statement:

☐.☐☐ to the nearest whole number is ☐

Find four different solutions.

READY?

When we count forwards and backwards we create a sequence of numbers. For example:

* Counting forwards in steps of 5, starting from 0

creates the sequence 0, 5, 10, 15, 20, 25, ...

* Counting backwards in steps of 3, starting from 50

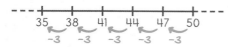

creates the sequence 50, 47, 44, 41, 38, 35, ...

e.g. 1 Count forwards in steps of 4, starting at 0

This means we start at 0 and 'add 4' each time

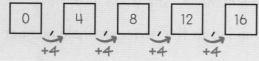

| 0 | , | 4 | , | 8 | , | 12 | , | 16 |

We can count forwards from other numbers ...

e.g. 2 The numbers in a sequence start with 15 and increase by 10 each time. Find the first five numbers.

① Start at 15

| 15 | , | 25 | , | 35 | , | 45 | , | 55 |

+10   +10   +10   +10

② 'add 10' each time

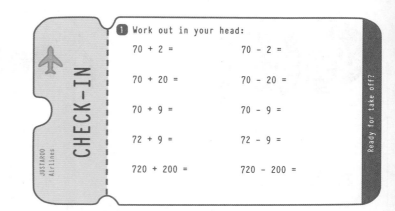

① Work out in your head:

70 + 2 =	70 − 2 =
70 + 20 =	70 − 20 =
70 + 9 =	70 − 9 =
72 + 9 =	72 − 9 =
720 + 200 =	720 − 200 =

CHECK-IN

JUSTAROO Airlines

Ready for take off?

e.g. 3 Create a sequence by counting backwards in steps of 9, starting at 80. Find the first six numbers.

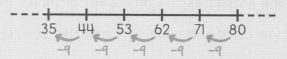

The sequence is 80, 71, 62, 53, 44, 35

We can use sequences to find missing numbers ...

e.g. 4 The numbers in a sequence decrease by the same amount each time. Find the missing numbers.

400 , 350 , 300 , ☐ , ☐

The numbers are decreasing by 50 each time

400 , 350 , 300 , 250 , 200

−50   −50

'Count backwards' means we need to subtract

SET?

A. Count forwards in steps of 3 starting from 0

| 0 | , | ☐ | , | ☐ | , | ☐ | , | ☐ |

B. The numbers in a sequence start with 0 and increase by 25 each time. Find the next four numbers.

| 0 | , | ☐ | , | ☐ | , | ☐ | , | ☐ |

C. The numbers in a sequence start with 14 and increase by 6 each time. Find the first five numbers.

| ☐ | , | ☐ | , | ☐ | , | ☐ | , | ☐ |

D. Create a sequence by counting backwards in steps of 5, starting at 100. Find the first five numbers.

E. Count backwards in steps of 30 starting from 200

| 200 | , | ☐ | , | ☐ | , | ☐ | , | ☐ |

F. The numbers in a sequence decrease by the same amount each time. Find the next three numbers.

| 1250 | , | 1150 | , | ☐ | , | ☐ | , | ☐ |

28

COUNTING AND SEQUENCES

10 , ☐ , ☐ , 100 , ☐

1. Tabitha is counting forwards in steps of the same number.

Find the missing numbers.

2. The numbers in this sequence decrease by the same amount each time.

103,352   102,352   101,352   100,352 ...

What is the next number in the sequence?

3. Simba is counting forwards in steps of 9 from zero. He writes:

0, 9, 19, 29, 39, ...

Do you agree? Explain your answer.

4. Robin is counting backwards from 250 in steps of 30

Jennifer is counting forwards from 0 in steps of 7

Find the only number that appears in both of their sequences.

5. Michelle is counting a pile of £20 notes.

She needs the total amount of money to be at least £150

What is the smallest number of notes she needs to count?

Negative numbers are numbers less than zero.

GETTING LARGER →

| -5 | -4 | -3 | -2 | -1 | 0 | 1 | 2 | 3 | 4 | 5 |

Negative numbers

Zero is neither positive nor negative

Positive numbers

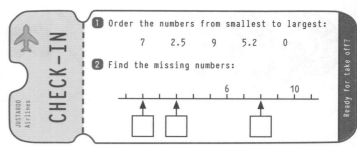

JUSTAROO Airlines

CHECK-IN

1 Order the numbers from smallest to largest:

7   2.5   9   5.2   0

2 Find the missing numbers:

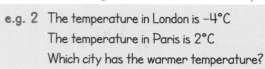

6   10

Ready for take off?

e.g. 1 Find the missing numbers on the number line.

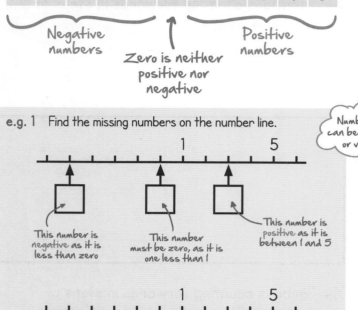

1   5

This number is negative as it is less than zero

This number must be zero, as it is one less than 1

This number is positive as it is between 1 and 5

Number lines can be horizontal or vertical

1   5

-4   0   3

Count 4 places backwards from 0

Count 2 places forwards from 1

We often see negative numbers as temperatures.

e.g. 2 The temperature in London is –4°C
The temperature in Paris is 2°C
Which city has the warmer temperature?

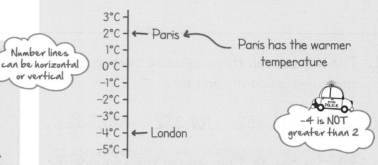

3°C
2°C ← Paris
1°C
0°C
–1°C
–2°C
–3°C
–4°C ← London
–5°C

Paris has the warmer temperature

–4 is NOT greater than 2

We can order positive and negative numbers.

e.g. 3 Place these temperatures in order from coldest to warmest:

6°C   –1°C   –4°C   3°C   1°C

Negative numbers   Positive numbers

–4°C   –1°C   1°C   3°C   6°C

–4°C is colder than –1°C

6°C is warmer than 3°C and 1°C

Negative numbers are numbers less than zero

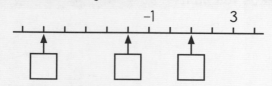

A. Find the missing numbers.

5   9

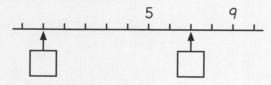

B. Find the missing numbers.

2   6

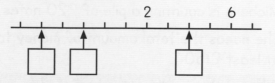

C. Find the missing numbers.

–1   3

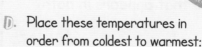

D. Place these temperatures in order from coldest to warmest:

–2°C   –5°C   1°C   3°C   –4°C

E. Place these temperatures in order from coldest to warmest:

3°C   –3°C   –6°C   9°C   0°C

F. The temperature in New York is –5°C
The temperature in Berlin is 1°C
Which city has the colder temperature?

NEGATIVE NUMBERS 1

1. Here is a sequence of numbers.

The difference between each pair of numbers is the same.

Find the missing numbers.

☐ ☐ 2 ☐ 10

2. The difference between two temperatures is 5°C.

Both temperatures are less than 0°C.

Find two possible pairs of temperatures.

3. Patsy writes:

−5°C is warmer than 2°C because 5 > 2

Do you agree? Explain your answer.

4. The temperature at 5:30 a.m. was recorded each day for one week.

Mon	Tue	Wed	Thu	Fri	Sat	Sun
−4°C	−1°C	0°C	−6°C	−2°C	−3°C	−5°C

a) On what day was the coldest morning?

b) On what day was the warmest morning?

c) What is the difference in temperature between the warmest and coldest temperatures?

m

5. A submarine is 50 metres below sea level.

A diver is 45 metres above the submarine.

How far below sea level is the diver?

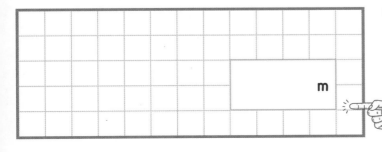

 **READY?**

When we subtract a larger number from a smaller number the answer is negative: e.g. $3 - 7 = -4$

-5 -4 -3 -2 -1 0 1 2 3 4 5

A number line is also helpful when adding numbers to a negative number: e.g. $-2 + 3 = 1$

-5 -4 -3 -2 -1 0 1 2 3 4 5

e.g. 1 $2 - 5 = \boxed{}$

1️⃣ Mark 2 on a number line

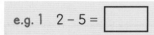

-5 -4 **-3** -2 -1 0 1 2 3 4 5

2️⃣ Count back 5 places   3️⃣ Read the answer

$2 - 5 = \boxed{-3}$

When the starting number is a negative number ...

e.g. 2 Calculate $-2 + 5$

1️⃣ Mark -2 on a number line

-5 -4 -3 -2 -1 0 1 2 **3** 4 5

2️⃣ Count forwards 5 places

3️⃣ $-2 + 5 = 3$

We can also subtract from a negative number ...

e.g. 3 $-1 - 3 = \boxed{}$

1️⃣ Mark -1 on a number line

-5 **-4** -3 -2 -1 0 1 2 3 4 5

2️⃣ Count back 3 places

3️⃣ $-1 - 3 = \boxed{-4}$

e.g. 4 Calculate the difference between 3 and -4

1️⃣ Mark 3 and -4 on a number line

-5 -4 -3 -2 -1 0 1 2 3 4 5

       4   3

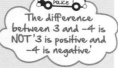

2️⃣ Calculate the distance between them using zero as a 'stopping point'

Difference = $4 + 3 = 7$

The difference between 3 and -4 is NOT '3 is positive and -4 is negative'

32

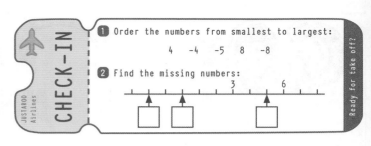
 **SET?**

A. (i) $1 - 4 = \boxed{}$ (ii) $5 - 7 = \boxed{}$

B. (i) $-2 + 6 = \boxed{}$ (ii) $\boxed{} = -4 + 5$

C. (i) $-2 - 1 = \boxed{}$ (ii) $-2 - 6 = \boxed{}$

D. (i) $-2 + 10 = \boxed{}$ (ii) $\boxed{} = -9 + 9$

E. Calculate the difference between -3 and 5

F. Calculate the difference between 7 and -2

 GO!

Astounding!

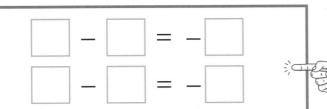

1. Complete the statements using only the digits 1, 2 and 3

2. Find a possible missing calculation by matching each calculation to its answer.

3 − 5	−8
−3 + 5	−5
1 − 6	−2
	2
−1 − 6	−7

3. Carly is trying to work out −5 + 7

She writes:

−5 + 7 = 1

because seven steps from −5 is

−5, −4, −3, −2, −1, 0, 1

Explain why Carly is not correct.

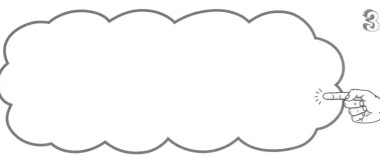

4. Jadon is staying at a hotel.

The car park is underground on floor '−2'

The lift goes up 7 floors to his room.

On what floor is Jadon's room?

5. The difference between the temperatures of two cities is 15°C.

Both temperatures have only one digit.

One temperature is negative.

One temperature is a prime number.

Find the temperatures of the two cities.

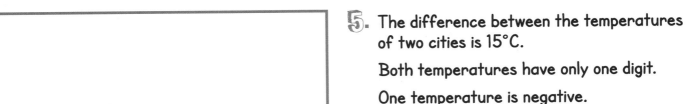

It is sometimes easier and more efficient to do a calculation using mental methods (in your head or with jottings), instead of using a written method. For example, mental methods would be useful for calculations such as:

| 450 + 200 | 746 + 99 |
| 240 + 150 | 4,326 + 3,999 |

It's always a good idea to first look at the types of numbers involved in the calculation and then make a decision about the most appropriate method.

e.g. 1 450 + 200 = ☐

450 + 200

Look at the numbers ... we are adding two HUNDRED to four HUNDRED and fifty

= 650

4 + 2 = 6 (hundreds)

450 + 200 = **650**

Sometimes jotting a number line will help ...

e.g. 2 240 + 150 = ☐

+100   +50

240   340   390

Partition 150 into 100 and 50

240 + 150 = **390**

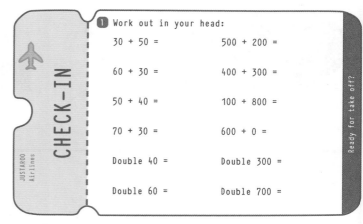

1 Work out in your head:

30 + 50 =	500 + 200 =
60 + 30 =	400 + 300 =
50 + 40 =	100 + 800 =
70 + 30 =	600 + 0 =
Double 40 =	Double 300 =
Double 60 =	Double 700 =

CHECK-IN

JUSTAROO Airlines

Ready for take off?

Another strategy is 'round and adjust' ...

e.g. 3 ☐ = 746 + 99

746 + 100 = 846

Look at the numbers ... 99 is one less than 100, so let's round 99 to 100

−1

845 = 746 + 99

Remember we are adding 99, not 100, so adjust by subtracting 1

e.g. 4 4,326 + 3,999 = ☐

4,326 + 4,000

3,999 is one less than 4,000 so round 3,999 to 4,000

= 8,326

−1

4,326 + 3,999 = **8,325**

Remember to adjust by subtracting 1

Think ... can I do the calculation in my head or with jottings?

SET?

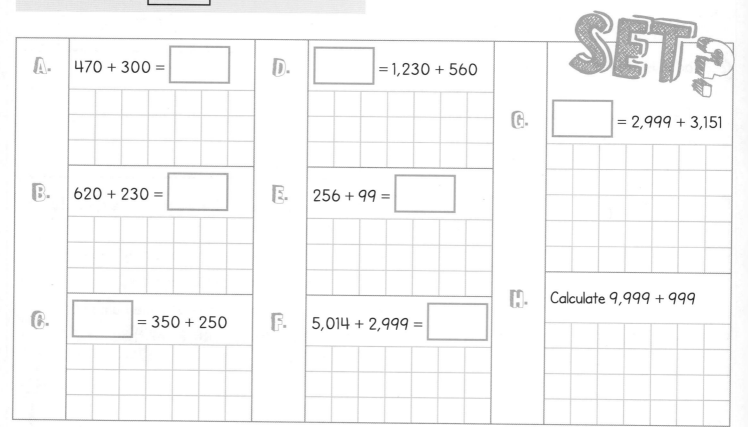

A. 470 + 300 = ☐

D. ☐ = 1,230 + 560

G. ☐ = 2,999 + 3,151

B. 620 + 230 = ☐

E. 256 + 99 = ☐

C. ☐ = 350 + 250

F. 5,014 + 2,999 = ☐

H. Calculate 9,999 + 999

MENTAL ADDITION

1. Calculate 9,999 + 999 + 99 + 9

2. Dani says,

"To add 999 to 470 you need to add 1,000 and then add 1.
So 470 + 999 = 1,471"

Explain why Dani is not correct.

3. Find the missing digits.

4,☐00 + 2☐0 = ☐,83☐

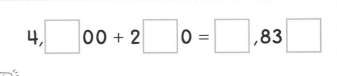

4. The table shows the number of pupils in each class at a school:

Class	Number of pupils
1A	199
2B	155
3C	202

How many pupils are there altogether at the school?

5. The numbers in the sequence increase by the same amount each time.

Find the missing numbers.

☐ 220 ☐ 460 ☐

It's a good idea to first look at the types of
numbers involved in any calculation. For example,
mental methods would be useful for calculations
such as:

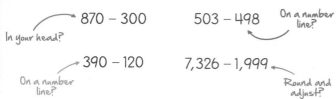

870 – 300   503 – 498   On a number line?

In your head?

390 – 120   7,326 – 1,999   Round and adjust?

On a number line?

e.g. 1 870 – 300 = [ ]

870 – 300   Look at the numbers ... we are subtracting
three HUNDRED from eight HUNDRED
and seventy

= 570   8 – 3 = 5 (hundreds)

870 – 300 = [570]

Sometimes jotting a number line will help ...

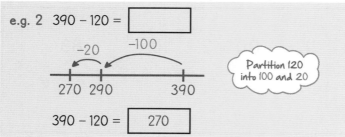

e.g. 2 390 – 120 = [ ]

–20   –100

270 290   390

Partition 120 into 100 and 20

390 – 120 = [270]

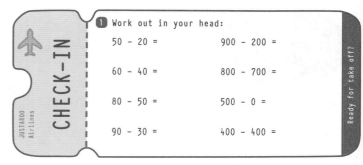

1 Work out in your head:

50 – 20 =   900 – 200 =

60 – 40 =   800 – 700 =

80 – 50 =   500 – 0 =

90 – 30 =   400 – 400 =

CHECK-IN

JUSTAROO Airlines

Ready for take off?

We could think about subtraction as 'difference'
and use 'counting on' ...

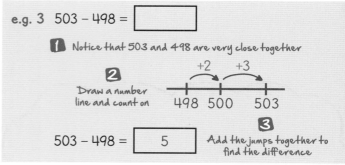

e.g. 3 503 – 498 = [ ]

1 Notice that 503 and 498 are very close together

2 Draw a number line and count on

+2   +3

498 500   503

503 – 498 = [5]

3 Add the jumps together to find the difference

We can also use 'round and adjust' ...

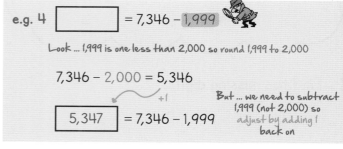

e.g. 4 [ ] = 7,346 – 1,999

Look ... 1,999 is one less than 2,000 so round 1,999 to 2,000

7,346 – 2,000 = 5,346

+1

[5,347] = 7,346 – 1,999

But ... we need to subtract 1,999 (not 2,000) so adjust by adding 1 back on

Think ... can I do the calculation in my head
or with jottings?

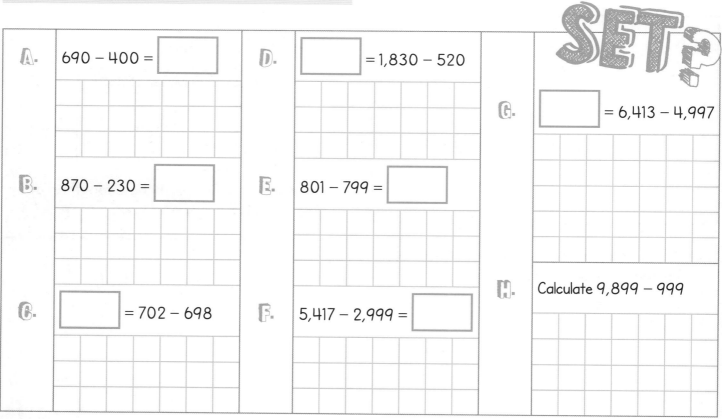

A. 690 – 400 = [ ]

D. [ ] = 1,830 – 520

G. [ ] = 6,413 – 4,997

B. 870 – 230 = [ ]

E. 801 – 799 = [ ]

C. [ ] = 702 – 698

F. 5,417 – 2,999 = [ ]

H. Calculate 9,899 – 999

GO!

MENTAL SUBTRACTION

Tidy!

1. Calculate 9,999 − 999 − 99 − 9

2. Find the missing digits.

$5,0\boxed{}\boxed{} - 4,9\boxed{}8 = 3$

3. Terry says,

"820 − 299 = 519 because you need to subtract 300 and then subtract 1"

Explain why Terry is not correct.

4. The table shows the number of visits to three websites in one week:

Website	Number of visits
MakingMathsGreat	1,697
MathsMan	4,005
MathsOClock	2,300

How many more visits were there to the MathsMan website than the total number of visits to the other two websites?

5. Match the calculations that have the same answer.

4,003 − 3,998	4,060 − 4,028
4,300 − 3,998	4,602 − 4,300
4,030 − 3,998	4,023 − 4,018

READY?

It's sensible to look at the numbers in a calculation to decide if a written method is suitable ... sometimes it's easier to do the calculation mentally (in our head or with jottings). The written method of addition involves adding columns of digits together. When regrouping, it is important to remember the value of each digit: e.g. 10 tens = 1 one hundred.

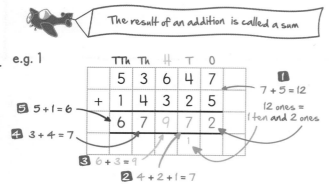

The result of an addition is called a sum

e.g. 1

	TTh	Th	H	T	O
	5	3	6	4	7
+	1	4	3	2	5
	6	7	9	7	2

1 7 + 5 = 12
12 ones = 1 ten and 2 ones

5 5 + 1 = 6
4 3 + 4 = 7
3 6 + 3 = 9
2 4 + 2 + 1 = 7

Sometimes we need to be careful with the carry digit ...

e.g. 2

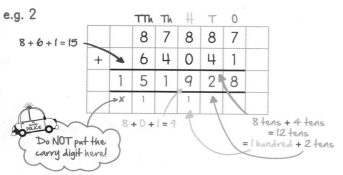

	TTh	Th	H	T	O
	8	7	8	8	7
+	6	4	0	4	1
	1	5	1	9	2	8

8 + 6 + 1 = 15

Do NOT put the carry digit here!

8 + 0 + 1 = 9

8 tens + 4 tens = 12 tens = 1 hundred + 2 tens

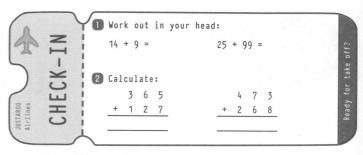

JUSTAROO Airlines — CHECK-IN — Ready for take off?

1 Work out in your head:

14 + 9 =   25 + 99 =

2 Calculate:

```
    3 6 5              4 7 3
  + 1 2 7            + 2 6 8
  _____            _____
```

Sometimes the number of digits is different ...

e.g. 3 Work out 53,674 + 5,863

These numbers have a different number of digits, so be careful to line up the ones with ones, tens with tens, etc.

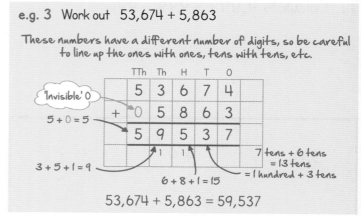

	TTh	Th	H	T	O
'Invisible' 0	5	3	6	7	4
+	0	5	8	6	3
	5	9	5	3	7

5 + 0 = 5
3 + 5 + 1 = 9
6 + 8 + 1 = 15
7 tens + 6 tens = 13 tens = 1 hundred + 3 tens

53,674 + 5,863 = 59,537

e.g. 4   ☐ = 93,674 + 9,253

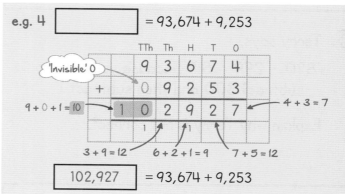

	TTh	Th	H	T	O
'Invisible' 0	9	3	6	7	4
+	0	9	2	5	3
	1	0	2	9	2	7

9 + 0 + 1 = 10
3 + 9 = 12
6 + 2 + 1 = 9
7 + 5 = 12
4 + 3 = 7

102,927 = 93,674 + 9,253

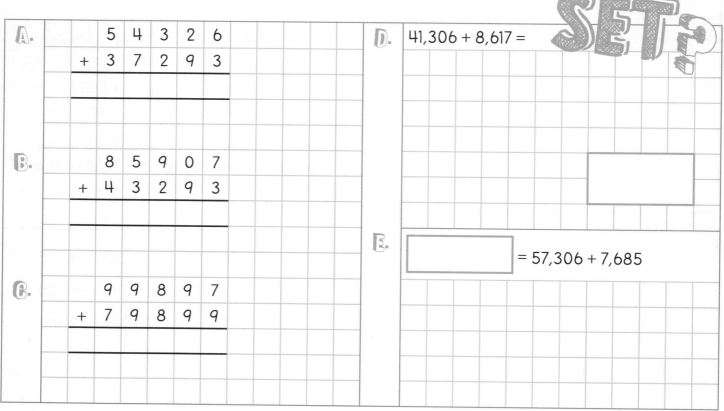

SET?

A.

	5	4	3	2	6
+	3	7	2	9	3

B.

	8	5	9	0	7
+	4	3	2	9	3

C.

	9	9	8	9	7
+	7	9	8	9	9

D. 41,306 + 8,617 =

☐

E. ☐ = 57,306 + 7,685

GO! WRITTEN METHODS: ADDITION

1. The distance from London to New York is 3,459 miles.

The distance from New York to Perth is 11,613 miles.

A plane flies from London to New York to Perth.

How far does the plane fly altogether?

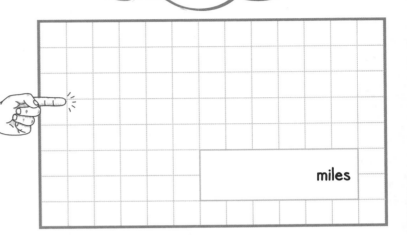

miles

---

2. Find the missing digits.

```
    2  7  □  2  □
  +    □  4  □  5
  ──────────────
  □  1  6  0  2
```

---

3. Kenny thinks the sum of 23,456 and 41,524 is 64,970. Here is his working:

		4	1	5	2	4
	+	2	3	4	5	6
		6	4	9	7	0
					1	

Explain why Kenny is not correct.

---

4. Tick the calculation with a sum closest to one hundred thousand.

9,678 + 73,477 □

82,178 + 17,806 □

45,698 + 54,698 □

59,999 + 39,987 □

READY?

The written method of subtraction involves taking digits away from each other within columns. It is important to remember the value of each digit when exchanging: e.g. 1 ten = 10 ones, 1 hundred = 10 tens, etc.

✈ CHECK-IN

JUSTAROO Airlines

Ready for take off?

1 Work out in your head:

21 − 8 =   34 − 9 =

2 Calculate:

```
    5 7 1              8 0 3
  − 2 4 8            − 4 7 6
  _____            _____
```

e.g. 1

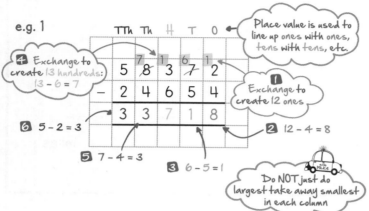

Place value is used to line up ones with ones, tens with tens, etc.

4 Exchange to create 13 hundreds: 13 − 6 = 7

1 Exchange to create 12 ones

```
        7   1   6   1
TTh Th  H   T   O
  5  8  3   7   2
− 2  4  6   5   4
  _____
  3  3  7   1   8
```

6 5 − 2 = 3

5 7 − 4 = 3

3 6 − 5 = 1

2 12 − 4 = 8

Do NOT just do largest take away smallest in each column

We may need to exchange twice (or more) in a row ...

e.g. 2

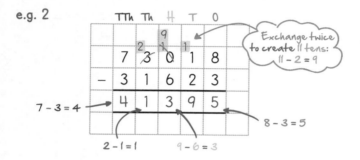

Exchange twice to create 11 tens: 11 − 2 = 9

```
      2  9  1
      1  1
TTh Th  H  T  O
  7  3  0  1  8
− 3  1  6  2  3
  _____
  4  1  3  9  5
```

7 − 3 = 4

2 − 1 = 1   9 − 6 = 3   8 − 3 = 5

e.g. 3 Calculate 23,081 − 1,749

As with addition, when there are a different number of digits be careful to line up the ones with ones etc.

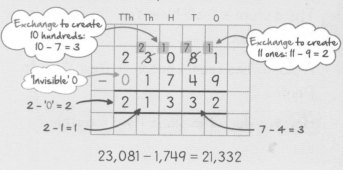

Exchange to create 10 hundreds: 10 − 7 = 3

'Invisible' 0

Exchange to create 11 ones: 11 − 9 = 2

```
      2   1   7   1
TTh Th    H   T   O
  2   3   0   8   1
− 0   1   7   4   9
  _____
  2   1   3   3   2
```

2 − '0' = 2

2 − 1 = 1   7 − 4 = 3

23,081 − 1,749 = 21,332

e.g. 4 | 35,432 | = 45,039 − 9,607

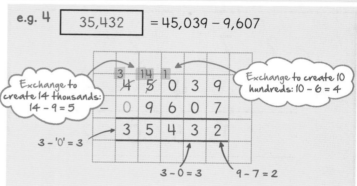

Exchange to create 14 thousands: 14 − 9 = 5

Exchange to create 10 hundreds: 10 − 6 = 4

```
  3  14  1
TTh Th  H  T  O
  4  5  0  3  9
− 0  9  6  0  7
  _____
  3  5  4  3  2
```

3 − '0' = 3   3 − 0 = 3   9 − 7 = 2

SET?

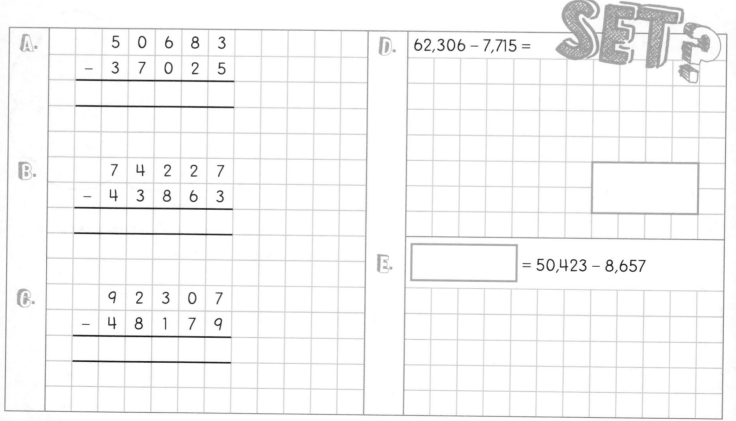

A.
```
    5 0 6 8 3
  − 3 7 0 2 5
  _____
```

B.
```
    7 4 2 2 7
  − 4 3 8 6 3
  _____
```

C.
```
    9 2 3 0 7
  − 4 8 1 7 9
  _____
```

D. 62,306 − 7,715 =

E. [   ] = 50,423 − 8,657

GO!

WRITTEN METHODS: SUBTRACTION

1. The attendance for two pop concerts is shown in the table:

Little Maths	27,867
Maths Direction	52,023

How many more people watched Maths Direction?

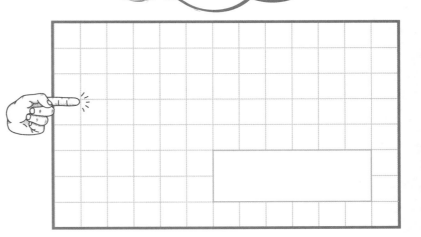

2. Find the missing digits.

```
    4  1  □  2  1
  -    □  6  1  □
    ─────────────
    □  7  3  □  5
    ─────────────
```

3. Ava thinks the difference between 23,072 and 49,543 is 26,531.

Here is her working:

```
    4  9  5  4  3
  - 2  3  0  7  2
    ─────────────
    2  6  5  3  1
```

Explain why Ava is not correct.

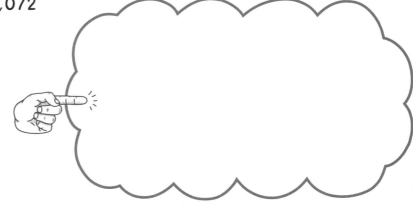

4. A 5-digit number and a 4-digit number are created using nine different digits.
Find:

a) the largest possible difference between the two numbers.

b) the smallest possible difference between the two numbers.

READY?

When we write or say a multiplication table such as:

5 × 1 = 5	5 × 5 = 25	5 × 9 = 45
5 × 2 = 10	5 × 6 = 30	5 × 10 = 50
5 × 3 = 15	5 × 7 = 35	5 × 11 = 55
5 × 4 = 20	5 × 8 = 40	5 × 12 = 60

the products (5, 10, 15, 20, 25, 30, 35, 40, 45, 50, 55, 60, ...) are known as multiples of 5

Of course, the list doesn't stop at 5 × 12 = 60 and so 65, 70, 75, 80, 85, ... are also multiples of 5

Multiples are the result of multiplying a number by an integer. For example, multiples of 10 are:

10 (10 × 1 = 10)

20 (10 × 2 = 20)

30 (10 × 3 = 30) ... and so on

e.g. 1 Find four multiples of 8

8 × 1 = 8
8 × 2 = 16
8 × 3 = 24
8 × 4 = 32

I, 2 and 4 are NOT multiples of 8 ... they are factors of 8

8, 16, 24 and 32 are multiples of 8

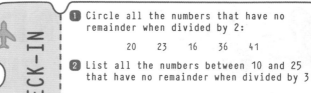

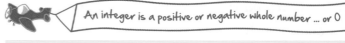
JUSTAROO Airlines

CHECK-IN

Ready for take off?

1 Circle all the numbers that have no remainder when divided by 2:

20   23   16   36   41

2 List all the numbers between 10 and 25 that have no remainder when divided by 3

3 Circle all the numbers that have no remainder when divided by 4:

10   20   30   40   50

An integer is a positive or negative whole number ... or 0

e.g. 2 How many multiples of 7 are between 30 and 45?

7 × 4 = 28
7 × 5 = 35
7 × 6 = 42
7 × 7 = 49

35 and 42 lie between 30 and 45

Two multiples of 7 are between 30 and 45

When finding multiples, it is useful to think about multiplication tables, but divisibility rules also help.

e.g. 3 Tick the multiples of 5

✓ 15   ← 5 × 3 = 15

☐ 42

✓ 55   ← 5 × 11 = 55

☐ 63

✓ 90   ← Multiples of 5 always end with 0 or 5

A. Find five multiples of 6

B. List the first five positive multiples of 15

SET?

A. Find five multiples of 11

B. How many multiples of 8 are between 30 and 50?

E. Tick the multiples of 3

☐ 9
☐ 13
☐ 21
☐ 45
☐ 73

MULTIPLES

1. Find the missing numbers:

$$\boxed{} + \boxed{} = \boxed{}$$

Multiple of 5   Multiple of 6   Multiple of 7

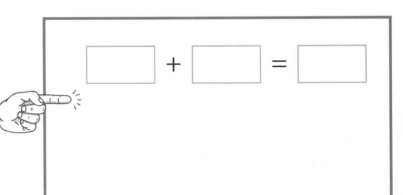

2. Claudia thinks that 4 is a multiple of 12

Explain why Claudia is not correct.

3. Find possible values for A, B and C.

Multiples of 12   Multiples of 20

A   B   C

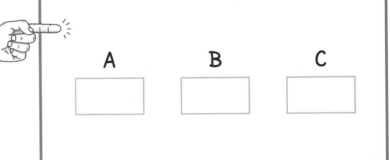

A   B   C

4. Bob runs around a running track in 5 minutes.

Sally runs around the same track in 4 minutes.

They start a race at 1 p.m.

At what time will they next cross the start line together?

HINT: Find the multiples of 4 and the multiples of 5

READY?
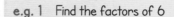

Factors are numbers that divide into another number with no remainder. Some numbers have only a few factors and some numbers have lots of factors.

CHECK-IN
JUSTAROO Airlines

Here is a list of numbers:
1   2   3   4   5

1 Choose two numbers that multiply together to give 5

2 Choose two numbers with a product of 8

3 Choose two numbers that multiply together to give 20

Ready for take off?

e.g. 1 Find the factors of 6

Make arrays using 6 counters:

○○○○○○ $1 \times 6 = 6$

$2 \times 3 = 6$

1, 2, 3 and 6 all divide into 6 with no remainder

The factors of 6 are 1, 2, 3 and 6

e.g. 2 Find the factors of 9

Make arrays using 9 counters:

$1 \times 9 = 9$ ●●●●●●●●●

$3 \times 3 = 9$

We only write the 3 once when listing the factors

The factors of 9 are 1, 3 and 9

A good way to find factors of a number is to use your multiplication tables knowledge to find 'factor pairs'.

e.g. 3 Find the factors of 12

$1 \times 12 = 12$
$2 \times 6 = 12$
$3 \times 4 = 12$
$4 \times 3 = 12$

STOP ... we have already used 4 (and 3) in a factor pair

The factors of 12 are 1, 2, 3, 4, 6 and 12

Two or more numbers will have at least one factor the same. Any factors that are the same are called 'common factors'.

e.g. 4 Find the common factors of 9 and 12

1 List the factors of both numbers

Factors of 9 are: 1, 3 and 9
Factors of 12 are: 1, 2, 3, 4, 6 and 12

2 Find the factors that are in both lists

1 and 3 are common factors of 9 and 12

When finding factors of a number, 1 and the number itself are always factors

A. Find all the factors of 8

C. Find all the factors of 16

SET?

B. Find all the factors of 15

D. Find the common factors of 14 and 20

E. Tick the factors of 11

☐ 1   ☐ 2
☐ 3   ☐ 4
☐ 5   ☐ 6
☐ 7   ☐ 8
☐ 9   ☐ 10
☐ 11

GO!

FACTORS

1. A and B are factors of 24

A and B have a difference of 4

Find all the possible pairs of values for A and B.

2. Bob thinks that all numbers have an even number of factors.

Do you agree? Explain your answer.

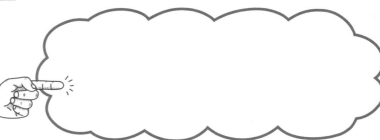

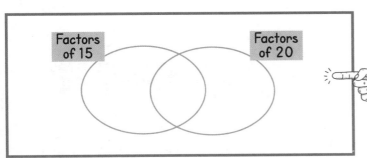

Factors of 15 | Factors of 20

3. Place the numbers

$$1 \quad 2 \quad 3 \quad 4 \quad 5$$

in the correct position in the diagram.

4. A perfect number is a number where the sum of the factors (not including the number itself) equals the number.

For example:

Factors of 8 are 1, 2, 4 and 8

$1 + 2 + 4 = 7$

This sum does not equal 8, so 8 is not a perfect number.

Find a perfect number between 2 and 10

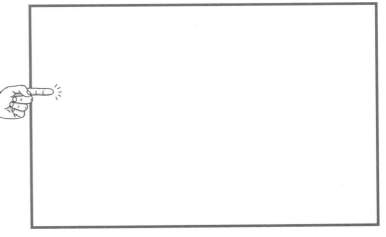

5. A number is between 40 and 50

The number has exactly 3 factors.

What is the number?

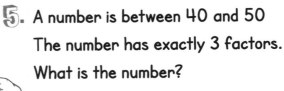

READY?

Not all numbers have the same number of factors:

Number	Factors	Number of factors
1	1	1
2	1, 2	2
3	1, 3	2
4	1, 2, 4	3
5	1, 5	2
6	1, 2, 3, 6	4

Numbers with exactly two factors are called **prime numbers**.

e.g. 1 Tick the numbers that are prime.

Number	7	8	9	10
Prime?	✓	✗	✗	✗

If we can draw more than one array, the number has more than two factors and so it is not prime

⬤⬤⬤⬤⬤⬤⬤

The factors of 7 are 1 and 7. It has exactly 2 factors.

prime

⬤⬤⬤⬤⬤⬤⬤⬤   ⬤⬤⬤⬤ / ⬤⬤⬤⬤

The factors of 8 are 1, 2, 4 and 8. It has 4 factors.

⬤⬤⬤⬤⬤⬤⬤⬤⬤   ⬤⬤⬤ / ⬤⬤⬤ / ⬤⬤⬤

The factors of 9 are 1, 3 and 9. It has 3 factors.

not prime

⬤⬤⬤⬤⬤⬤⬤⬤⬤⬤   ⬤⬤⬤⬤⬤ / ⬤⬤⬤⬤⬤

The factors of 10 are 1, 2, 5 and 10. It has 4 factors.

✈ CHECK-IN

1. Circle the number that is not a factor of 8:

    1   2   4   8   16

2. True or false: 4 is a factor 5?

3. True or false: 1 is a factor 9?

4. True or false: 15 is a factor 5?

5. True or false: 7 is a factor 7?

Ready for take off?

Sometimes we need to solve problems involving prime numbers.

e.g. 2 Find every pair of prime numbers with a sum of 20

The prime numbers less than 20 are:

2, 3, 5, 7, 11, 13, 17 and 19

Possible pairs are:

3 and 17   (3 + 17 = 20)

7 and 13   (7 + 13 = 20)

'sum' means the total of an addition

Sometimes we need to explain our reasoning.

e.g. 3 'Numbers with a 3 as a ones digit are prime numbers'. Do you agree? Explain your answer.

Don't be tricked into thinking something is true because it works for some numbers. In this case, it might seem to be true as 3, 13 and 23 are prime numbers.

No. 33 has a 3 as a ones digit, but 33 is not a prime number as it has four factors (1, 3, 11 and 33).

This is a COUNTER-EXAMPLE. It is a good way to prove that something is not correct.

A number with exactly 2 factors is called a PRIME number. A number with more than 2 factors is called a COMPOSITE number.

A. How many prime numbers are there between 1 and 20?

C. Find every pair of prime numbers with a sum of 18

SET?

B. List all the prime numbers between 20 and 30

D. Write down all the even prime numbers.

E. Tick the prime numbers:

- [ ] 9
- [ ] 19
- [ ] 29
- [ ] 39
- [ ] 49

 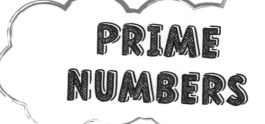

PRIME NUMBERS

1. Use the digits 2, 3, 4, 5, 7 and 9 to create three two-digit prime numbers.

2. Sancho thinks he has found a pattern:

If a number ends in a 7 it is a prime number

Do you agree with Sancho?
Explain your answer.

3. Alice is thinking of two prime numbers.

Both prime numbers are less than 20

The difference between the two prime numbers is 2

Find all the possible pairs of prime numbers.

4. Use four different numbers between 1 and 20 to complete the table.

	Prime number	Multiple of 4
Factor of 8		
Sum of the digits is 8		

5. An emirp ("prime" spelt backwards) is a prime number that when written in reverse is also a prime number.

For example, 13 is an emirp number because 31 is also prime.

Find all the emirp numbers up to 75

NOTE: 11 is not an emirp number because the digits must be different

 # READY?

CHECK-IN
JUSTAROO Airlines

1. Work out in your head:

    1 x 1 =   6 x 6 =

2. Circle the answer to 11 x 11:

    110   121   111   22

3. True or false: 12 x 12 = 144?

Ready for take off?

Numbers can be arranged as different shapes.

For example: 6 counters can be arranged as ...

a rectangle: or a triangle:

9 counters can be arranged as a square:

Numbers that can be arranged as a square are called **square numbers**.

OTHER STUFF ABOUT SQUARE NUMBERS:

Square numbers can be calculated by multiplying whole numbers by themselves: e.g. $3 \times 3 = 9$

We can write 3×3 as 3^2 ... we say this as '3 squared'

e.g. 1   Tick to show which numbers are square numbers.

Number	4	5	6	7	8	9	10
Square?							

4 and 9 can be arranged as squares:

$2 \times 2 = 4$ $3 \times 3 = 9$

4 is a square number because 2 multiplied by itself is 4

9 is a square number because 3 multiplied by itself is 9

5, 6, 7, 8 and 10 cannot be arranged as squares:

$1 \times 5 = 5$ $2 \times 3 = 6$ $1 \times 7 = 7$
                      (or $1 \times 6 = 6$)

$4 \times 2 = 8$ $5 \times 2 = 10$
(or $1 \times 8 = 8$)   (or $1 \times 10 = 10$)

The square numbers are 4 and 9

Number	4	5	6	7	8	9	10
Square?	✓	✗	✗	✗	✗	✓	✗

e.g. 2   Find the value of 4 squared.

'4 squared' means 4 multiplied by itself

4 squared = $4 \times 4 = 16$

e.g. 3   Work out 5^2

5^2 means 5 squared

$5^2 = 5 \times 5 = 25$

5^2 does NOT mean 5×2

A square number is the result of multiplying a whole number by itself

A.   Tick to show the square numbers.

Number	15	16	17	18	19	20	21	22	23	24	25
Square?											

B.   Work out:

(i)   2 squared

(ii) 7 squared

(iii) 8 squared

(iv) 10 squared

C.   Find the value of:

(i) 1^2

(ii) 3^2

(iii) 6^2

(iv) 9^2

D.   Write down the square numbers between 90 and 150

1. Find two different solutions to this problem:

$\boxed{}$ + $\boxed{}$ = $\boxed{}$

Square number   Square number   Square number

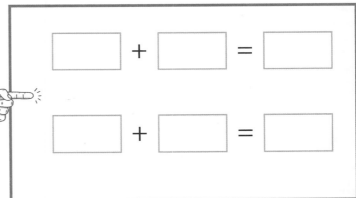

2. Sandra writes:

$$7^2 = 14$$

Do you agree? Explain your answer.

3. Find the missing consecutive numbers.

$\boxed{}$, $\boxed{}$, $\boxed{}$

Multiple of 6   Square number   Factor of 100

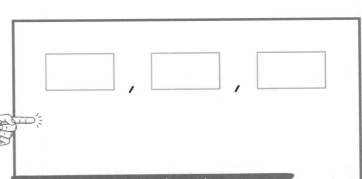

NOTE: 'Consecutive' means 'next to'; e.g. 21, 22, 23

4. A cube number is the result of multiplying a whole number by itself, then by itself again.

For example, the first cube number is 1 because:

$$1 \times 1 \times 1 = 1$$

Find the next four cube numbers.

READY?

It is important to recall and use the multiplication and division facts up to 12×12 ... these can be the trickiest to remember:

$3 \times 3 = 9$	$4 \times 6 = 24$	$6 \times 9 = 54$	$8 \times 9 = 72$
$3 \times 4 = 12$	$4 \times 7 = 28$	$6 \times 11 = 66$	$8 \times 11 = 88$
$3 \times 6 = 18$	$4 \times 8 = 32$	$6 \times 12 = 72$	$8 \times 12 = 96$
$3 \times 7 = 21$	$4 \times 9 = 36$	$7 \times 7 = 49$	$9 \times 9 = 81$
$3 \times 8 = 24$	$4 \times 11 = 44$	$7 \times 8 = 56$	$9 \times 11 = 99$
$3 \times 9 = 27$	$4 \times 12 = 48$	$7 \times 9 = 63$	$9 \times 12 = 108$
$3 \times 11 = 33$	$6 \times 6 = 36$	$7 \times 11 = 77$	$11 \times 11 = 121$
$3 \times 12 = 36$	$6 \times 7 = 42$	$7 \times 12 = 84$	$11 \times 12 = 132$
$4 \times 4 = 16$	$6 \times 8 = 48$	$8 \times 8 = 64$	$12 \times 12 = 144$

Top tip: If you forget a multiplication fact, you can always work it out using other facts ...

* if we know $10\times$ we can work out $5\times$ by halving,

* if we know $2\times$ we can work out $4\times$ by doubling ... and $8\times$ by doubling again.

e.g. 1 $4 \times 9 = \boxed{}$

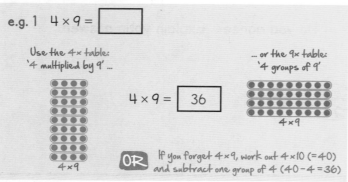

Use the 4× table: '4 multiplied by 9' ...

... or the 9× table: '4 groups of 9'

$4 \times 9 = \boxed{36}$

4×9

OR If you forget 4×9, work out $4 \times 10 (=40)$ and subtract one group of 4 $(40 - 4 = 36)$

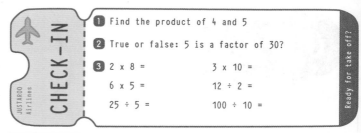

JUSTAROO Airlines · CHECK-IN · Ready for take off?

1. Find the product of 4 and 5
2. True or false: 5 is a factor of 30?
3. $2 \times 8 =$ $3 \times 10 =$
    $6 \times 5 =$ $12 \div 2 =$
    $25 \div 5 =$ $100 \div 10 =$

e.g. 2 $24 \div 4 = \boxed{}$

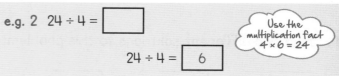

Use the multiplication fact $4 \times 6 = 24$

$24 \div 4 = \boxed{6}$

It is helpful to remember the multiplication table facts as **factor-factor-product** relationships: e.g. we can use 4/7/28 to recall multiplication and division facts.

e.g. 3 Using the fact $4 \times 7 = 28$ write three other statements using multiplication and division symbols.

$7 \times 4 = 28$

$28 \div 4 = 7$

$28 \div 7 = 4$

Remember: the order doesn't matter with multiplication (it's commutative)

e.g. 4 Complete the multiplication grid

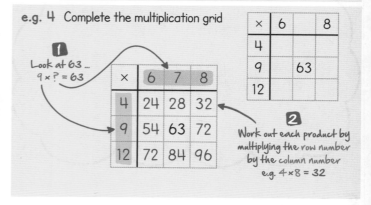

1. Look at 63 ... $9 \times ? = 63$

×	6	7	8
4	24	28	32
9	54	63	72
12	72	84	96

×	6		8
4			
9	63		
12			

2. Work out each product by multiplying the row number by the column number e.g. $4 \times 8 = 32$

SET?

A. $8 \times 9 = \boxed{}$

B. $7 \times 7 = \boxed{}$

C. $9 \times 9 = \boxed{}$

D. $11 \times 12 = \boxed{}$

E. $42 \div 7 = \boxed{}$

F. $108 \div 12 = \boxed{}$

G. Using the fact $8 \times 9 = 72$ complete the statements:

$\boxed{} \div \boxed{} = \boxed{}$

$\boxed{} \times \boxed{} = \boxed{}$

$\boxed{} \div \boxed{} = \boxed{}$

H. Complete the multiplication grid.

×	6	9	11
4			
			77
12			

I. Complete the multiplication grid.

×	6	8		4	3
	72				
					21
		45			
11		55			
		48			

GO! MULTIPLICATION TABLES

Fab!

1. Complete the multiplication grid.

×			
	18	24	
		56	21
	48		

2. Nik says, "When multiplying two numbers, you can change the order and get the same answer"

Tom says, "When dividing one number by a different number, you can change the order and get the same answer"

Tick the correct statement.

☐	Nik and Tom are both correct
☐	Only Nik is correct
☐	Only Tom is correct
☐	Neither Nik nor Tom are correct

3. Complete the statement using four different pairs of whole numbers.

☐ × ☐ = 24

☐ × ☐ = 24

☐ × ☐ = 24

☐ × ☐ = 24

☐ × ☐ = 24

4. Put the calculations in order of their answer from smallest to largest.

63 ÷ 7	1st	Smallest
64 ÷ 8	2nd	
121 ÷ 11	3rd	
42 ÷ 6	4th	
108 ÷ 9	5th	
60 ÷ 12	6th	Largest

5. An egg box holds 6 eggs. How many egg boxes can be completely filled with 55 eggs?

Numbers can be multiplied by 10 or 100 (or 1,000 etc.) using place value. When we multiply a number by 10, the digits move ONE column to the left.
For example, $13 \times 10 = 130$

Hundreds	Tens	Ones
	1	3
1	3	0

When we multiply a number by 10 it gets 10 times larger

Insert zero as a place value holder

When we multiply by 100 the digits move TWO columns to the left. For example, $13 \times 100 = 1,300$

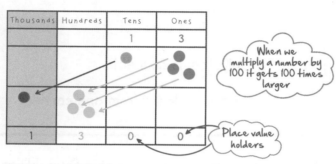

Thousands	Hundreds	Tens	Ones
		1	3
1	3	0	0

When we multiply a number by 100 it gets 100 times larger

Place value holders

If ×10, all digits move one column to the left
If ×100, all digits move two columns to the left

JUSTAROO Airlines

CHECK-IN

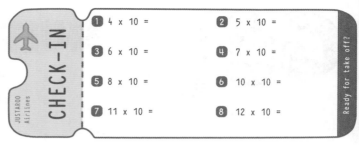

1 4 x 10 = | 2 5 x 10 =
3 6 x 10 = | 4 7 x 10 =
5 8 x 10 = | 6 10 x 10 =
7 11 x 10 = | 8 12 x 10 =

Ready for take off?

Multiplying by 10 ...

e.g. 1 Work out 43×10

H	T	O
	4	3
4	3	0

Move each digit ONE column to the left

$43 \times 10 = 430$

e.g. 2 Work out 205×10

Th	H	T	O
	2	0	5
2	0	5	0

Move each digit ONE column to the left

$205 \times 10 = 2,050$

Multiplying by 100 ...

e.g. 3 Calculate 78×100

Th	H	T	O
		7	8
7	8	0	0

Move each digit TWO columns to the left

$78 \times 100 = 7,800$

e.g. 4 Work out 305×100

TTh	Th	H	T	O
		3	0	5
3	0	5	0	0

Move each digit TWO columns to the left

$305 \times 100 = 30,500$

A. Work out:

(i) 35×10

(ii) 51×10

(iii) 70×10

(iv) 10×94

B. Calculate:

(i) 298×10

(ii) 571×10

(iii) 600×10

(iv) 10×801

C. Calculate:

(i) 67×100

(ii) 43×100

(iii) 58×100

(iv) 100×96

D. Work out:

(i) 167×100

(ii) 403×100

(iii) 100×580

(iv) 100×100

SET?

E. Write down the number 10 times greater than two hundred and seventy.

F. Write down the number 100 times greater than three hundred and sixteen.

MULTIPLYING BY 10 OR 100 PART 1

1. Find the missing number.

$$\boxed{} \times 100 = 60,400$$

---

2. A packet of sweets costs 13p

How much do 100 packets cost?

£ [ ]

---

3. Lois writes:

$$306 \times 10 = 3006$$

Do you agree? Explain your answer.

---

4. Match each calculation with its answer.

Find two possibilities for the missing calculation.

$6,002 \times 10$	6,200
602×100	6,020
	60,020
602×10	62,000
620×100	60,200

---

5. Tina runs 10 laps of a 250 metre track.

Ceri runs 2 kilometres.

Who runs the furthest and by how much?

HINT: 1 kilometre = 1,000 metres

READY?

Decimal numbers can be multiplied by 10 or 100 (or 1,000 etc.) using place value. Remember ... when we multiply any number by 10, the digits move ONE column to the left. For example, $1.3 \times 10 = 13$

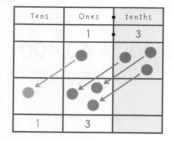

Tens	Ones	.	tenths
	1	.	3
1	3		

When we multiply a number by 10 it gets 10 times larger

And when we multiply by 100 the digits move TWO columns to the left. For example $1.3 \times 100 = 130$

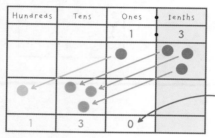

Hundreds	Tens	Ones	.	tenths
		1	.	3
1	3	0		

When we multiply a number by 100 it gets 100 times larger

Place value holder

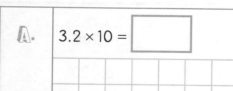

If ×10, all digits move one column to the left
If ×100, all digits move two columns to the left

CHECK-IN

JUSTAROO Airlines

1. Calculate 36 x 100
2. Circle the answer to 24 x 10:

   204   240   2,400   2,040
3. Write down the value of the digit 2 in the number 3.24
4. Write down the value of the digit 7 in the number 18.97

Ready for take off?

Multiplying by 10 ...

e.g. 1 Work out 4.23×10

H	T	O	.	t	h
		4	.	2	3
	4	2	.	3	

Move each digit ONE column to the left

$4.23 \times 10 = 42.3$

e.g. 2 Work out 0.32×10

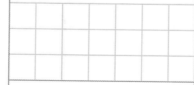
Do NOT write a zero here

H	T	O	.	t	h
		0	.	3	2
	3	.	2		

Move each digit ONE column to the left

$0.32 \times 10 = 3.2$

Multiplying by 100 ...

e.g. 3 Calculate 7.8×100

H	T	O	.	t	h
		7	.	8	
7	8	0	.		

Move each digit TWO columns to the left

$7.8 \times 100 = 780$

e.g. 4 Work out 0.305×100

H	T	O	.	t	h	th
		0	.	3	0	5
	3	0	.	5		

Move each digit TWO columns to the left

$0.305 \times 100 = 30.5$

SET?

A. $3.2 \times 10 = \boxed{}$

B. Calculate 0.17×10

C. Work out 4.6×100

D. Calculate 0.203×100

E. $0.203 \times 10 = \boxed{}$

F. What is 10 times greater than 3.02?

G. Work out 40.506×100

H. What is 100 times greater than 3.204?

54

MULTIPLYING BY 10 OR 100 PART 2

Solid!

1. Put a ring around the number that is 100 times larger than 7.05

> 70.5   7.0500   7,050   705   70,500

2. A length of ribbon is 8.5 centimetres.

> What is the total length of 100 pieces of this ribbon?

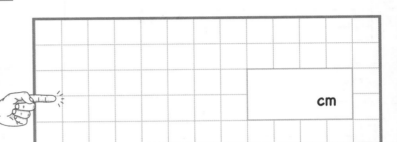

cm

3. Emma writes:

$$1.2 \times 100 = 1.200$$

Do you agree? Explain your answer.

4. Always true / Sometimes true / Never true:

> When you multiply a decimal by 100, the number of digits in the product is greater than the number of digits in the decimal

Explain your answer.

5. Tick the calculations with a product of 6.2

- 0.62×10
- 0.062×10
- 0.062×100
- 0.62×100
- 0.602×10
- 0.602×100

READY?

Numbers can be divided by 10 or 100 (or 1,000 etc.) using place value. When we divide a number by 10, the digits move ONE column to the right.
For example, 140 ÷ 10 = 14

Hundreds	Tens	Ones
1	4	0
	1	4

> When we divide a number by 10 it gets 10 times smaller

When we divide by 100 the digits move TWO columns to the right. For example, 140 ÷ 100 = 1.4

Hundreds	Tens	Ones	tenths
1	4	0	
		1	4

> When we divide a number by 100 it gets 100 times smaller

 If ÷10, all digits move one column to the right
If ÷100, all digits move two columns to the right

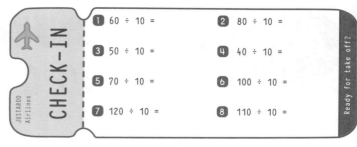

JUSTAROO Airlines | CHECK-IN

❶ 60 ÷ 10 =	❷ 80 ÷ 10 =
❸ 50 ÷ 10 =	❹ 40 ÷ 10 =
❺ 70 ÷ 10 =	❻ 100 ÷ 10 =
❼ 120 ÷ 10 =	❽ 110 ÷ 10 =

Ready for take off?

Dividing by 10 ...

e.g. 1 Work out 420 ÷ 10

H	T	O	.	t
4	2	0		
		4	.	2	0

> Move each digit ONE column to the right

420 ÷ 10 = 42
(We write 42.0 as 42)

e.g. 2 Work out 2,405 ÷ 10

Th	H	T	O	.	t
2	4	0	5		
	2	4	0	.	5

> Move each digit ONE column to the right

2,405 ÷ 10 = 240.5

Dividing by 100 ...

e.g. 3 Calculate 152 ÷ 100

H	T	O	.	h
1	5	2		
		1	.	5	2

> Move each digit TWO columns to the right

152 ÷ 100 = 1.52

e.g. 4 Work out 3,006 ÷ 100

Th	H	T	O	.	t	h
3	0	0	6			
		3	0	.	0	6

> Do NOT cancel zeros ... 3,006 ÷ 100 is NOT 36

3,006 ÷ 100 = 30.06

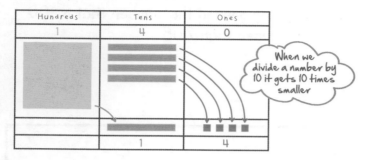

SET?

A. Work out:

(i) 240 ÷ 10

(ii) 570 ÷ 10

(iii) 780 ÷ 10

(iv) 910 ÷ 10

B. Calculate:

(i) 3,601 ÷ 10

(ii) 5,708 ÷ 10

(iii) 278 ÷ 10

(iv) 91 ÷ 10

C. Calculate:

(i) 243 ÷ 100

(ii) 567 ÷ 100

(iii) 708 ÷ 100

(iv) 923 ÷ 100

D. Work out:

(i) 9,003 ÷ 100

(ii) 2,671 ÷ 100

(iii) 4,708 ÷ 100

(iv) 17,050 ÷ 100

E. Write down the number 10 times smaller than three thousand and fifty.

F. Write down the number 100 times smaller than three hundred and forty.

G. Write down the number 100 times smaller than two thousand and twenty-one.

GO!

DIVIDING BY 10 OR 100 PART 1

1. Find the missing number.

$$\boxed{} \div 100 = 5.6$$

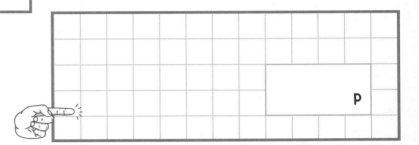

2. Freda pays £56 for 100 roses.

   How much does one rose cost?

3. Always true / Sometimes true / Never true:

   To divide a number by 100 you can divide by 10 and then divide by 10 again

   Explain your answer.

4. Match each calculation with its answer.

   Find two possibilities for the missing calculation.

206 ÷ 10	2.06
2,006 ÷ 100	20.6
206 ÷ 100	20.6
	20.06
206 ÷ 10	200.6

5. Mitch has a 2.5 litre bottle of water.

   The amount of water in a glass is 10 times smaller than the bottle.

   How many millilitres of water are in the glass?

   $$\boxed{} \text{ ml}$$

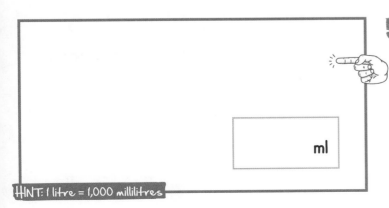

HINT: 1 litre = 1,000 millilitres

Decimal numbers can be divided by 10 or 100 (or 1,000 etc.) using place value. Remember ... when we divide any number by 10, the digits move ONE column to the right. For example, $13.2 \div 10 = 1.32$

T	O	.	t	h
1	3	.	2	
		.		
		.		
	1	.	3	2

When we divide a number by 10 it gets 10 times smaller

And when we divide by 100 the digits move TWO columns to the right. For example, $213.4 \div 100 = 2.134$

H	T	O	.	t	h	th
2	1	3	.	4		
			.			
		2	.	1	3	4

When we divide a number by 100 it gets 100 times smaller

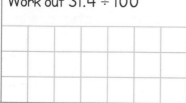

If ÷10, all digits move one column to the right
If ÷100, all digits move two columns to the right

Dividing by 10 ...

e.g. 1 Work out $4.2 \div 10$

H	T	O	.	t	h
		4	.	2	
		0	.	4	2

Place value holder

Move each digit ONE column to the right

$4.2 \div 10 = 0.42$

e.g. 2 Work out $10.6 \div 10$

H	T	O	.	t	h
	1	0	.	6	
		1	.	0	6

Move each digit ONE column to the right

$10.6 \div 10 = 1.06$

Dividing by 100 ...

e.g. 3 Calculate $12.3 \div 100$

H	T	O	.	t	h	th
	1	2	.	3		
		0	.	1	2	3

Move each digit TWO columns to the right

$12.3 \div 100 = 0.123$

e.g. 4 Work out $0.3 \div 100$

H	T	O	.	t	h	th
		0	.	3		
		0	.	0	0	3

Move each digit TWO columns to the right

$0.3 \div 100 = 0.003$

A. $3.8 \div 10 = \boxed{}$

B. Calculate $70.3 \div 10$

C. Work out $31.4 \div 100$

D. Calculate $0.2 \div 100$

E. $2.1 \div 100 = \boxed{}$

F. What is 10 times smaller than 37.23?

G. Work out $0.09 \div 10$

H. What is 100 times smaller than 324.6?

1. Find the missing number.

$$\boxed{} \div 100 = 5.6$$

2. Shop A is selling boxes of 100 pens for £12.50

Shop B is selling boxes of 10 pens for £1.35

Which shop is offering the best deal? Give a reason for your answer.

3. Ene writes:

$$400.5 \div 100 = 4.5$$

Do you agree? Explain your answer.

4. Tick the calculations with the answer 0.023

$2.3 \div 10$

$2.03 \div 10$

$0.203 \div 10$

$20.3 \div 100$

$0.23 \div 10$

$2.3 \div 100$

5. Complete the diagram by writing ×10, ×100, ÷10 or ÷100 in the arrows.

4.5 ⟩ 0.045 ⟩ 0.45 ⟩ 45

READY?

It is powerful in mathematics to use one fact to work out other facts. Making connections is very important.

For example, we can calculate 30×5 using the multiplication tables fact $3 \times 5 = 15$ and place value:

$$30 \times 5 = 3 \times 10 \times 5$$
$$= 15 \times 10$$
$$= 150$$

Remember:
When multiplying by 10, digits move one column to the left

$3 \times 5 = 15$ $30 \times 5 = 150$

30 is 10 times larger than 3 so the product will be 10 times larger

e.g. 1 $60 \times 7 = \boxed{}$

$$60 \times 7 = 6 \times 10 \times 7$$
$$= 42 \times 10$$
$$= 420$$

Remember:
$6 \times 7 = 42$

$60 \times 7 = \boxed{420}$

1 Write the answer to:

$3 \times 4 =$	$4 \times 7 =$	$6 \times 8 =$
$3 \times 6 =$	$9 \times 9 =$	$8 \times 12 =$
$4 \times 4 =$	$3 \times 12 =$	$7 \times 8 =$
$11 \times 9 =$	$3 \times 3 =$	$7 \times 12 =$
$8 \times 9 =$	$6 \times 4 =$	$8 \times 3 =$
$6 \times 6 =$	$8 \times 8 =$	$11 \times 3 =$
$3 \times 7 =$	$8 \times 11 =$	$4 \times 9 =$

e.g. 2 $\boxed{} = 600 \times 7$

$$600 \times 7 = 6 \times 100 \times 7$$
$$= 42 \times 100$$
$$= 4,200$$

$\boxed{4,200} = 600 \times 7$

e.g. 3   Calculate 60×70

$6 \times 7 = 42$
$60 \times 7 = 420$ $\times 10$
$60 \times 70 = 4,200$ $\times 10$

OR

60×70
$= 6 \times 10 \times 7 \times 10$
$= 42 \times 100$
$= 4,200$

If I know ...   then I also know ...

SET?

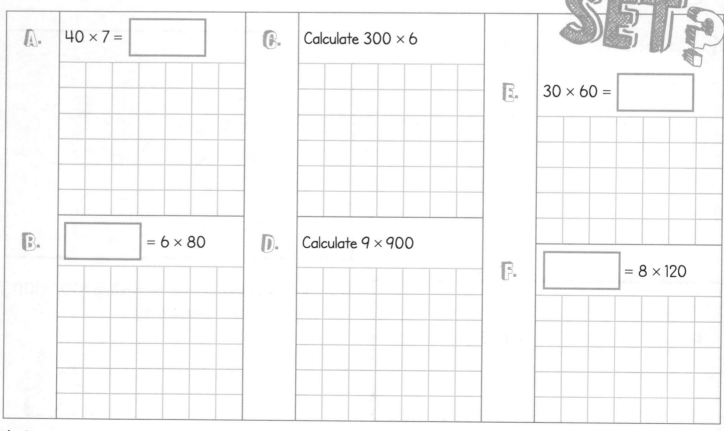

A. $40 \times 7 = \boxed{}$

B. $\boxed{} = 6 \times 80$

C.   Calculate 300×6

D.   Calculate 9×900

E. $30 \times 60 = \boxed{}$

F. $\boxed{} = 8 \times 120$

MENTAL MULTIPLICATION

1. Complete the calculation using the digits 5, 6, 7 and 8

$$\boxed{}0 \times \boxed{}0 = \boxed{},\boxed{}00$$

2. Mandy writes:

$$6 \times 500 = 3{,}000$$

Do you agree? Explain your answer.

3. There are 30 pupils in a class.

The school has 12 classes.

How many pupils are in the school in total?

4. Tick the calculations with a product greater than one thousand.

80×12	☐
30×30	☐
9×120	☐
300×4	☐
110×9	☐

5. Tony earns £700 per month. How much does he earn in total in one year?

READY?

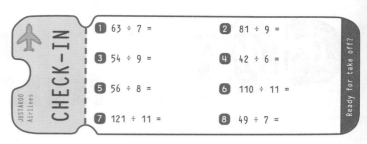

CHECK-IN

JUSTAROO Airlines

1. 63 ÷ 7 =
2. 81 ÷ 9 =
3. 54 ÷ 9 =
4. 42 ÷ 6 =
5. 56 ÷ 8 =
6. 110 ÷ 11 =
7. 121 ÷ 11 =
8. 49 ÷ 7 =

Ready for take off?

We can use division facts from the multiplication tables and knowledge of place value to divide larger numbers.

For example, we can calculate $120 ÷ 3$ using the known fact $12 ÷ 3 = 4$ and place value:

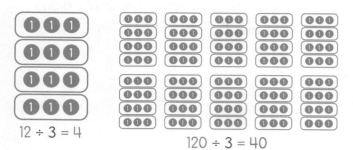

$12 ÷ 3 = 4$

$120 ÷ 3 = 40$

So ... when there are 10 times as many counters (120 instead of 12), dividing into groups of 3 gives 10 times as many groups (40 instead of 4)

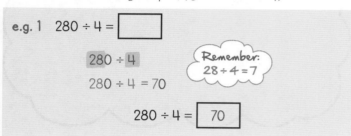

e.g. 1 $280 ÷ 4 = \boxed{}$

$280 ÷ 4$

$280 ÷ 4 = 70$

Remember:
$28 ÷ 4 = 7$

$280 ÷ 4 = \boxed{70}$

e.g. 2 Calculate $4,500 ÷ 5$

$4,500 ÷ 5$

$4,500 ÷ 5 = 900$

Remember:
$45 ÷ 5 = 9$

e.g. 3 $\boxed{} = 1,440 ÷ 12$

$1,440 ÷ 12$

$1,440 ÷ 12 = 120$

Remember:
$144 ÷ 12 = 12$

$\boxed{120} = 1,440 ÷ 12$

Be careful with the number of zeros ...

e.g. 4 $4,000 ÷ 8 = \boxed{}$

$4,000 ÷ 8$

$4,000 ÷ 8 = 500$

Remember:
$40 ÷ 8 = 5$

The answer is NOT 5,000

$4,000 ÷ 8 = \boxed{500}$

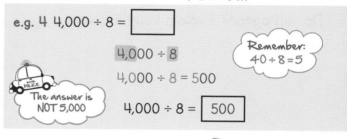

SET?

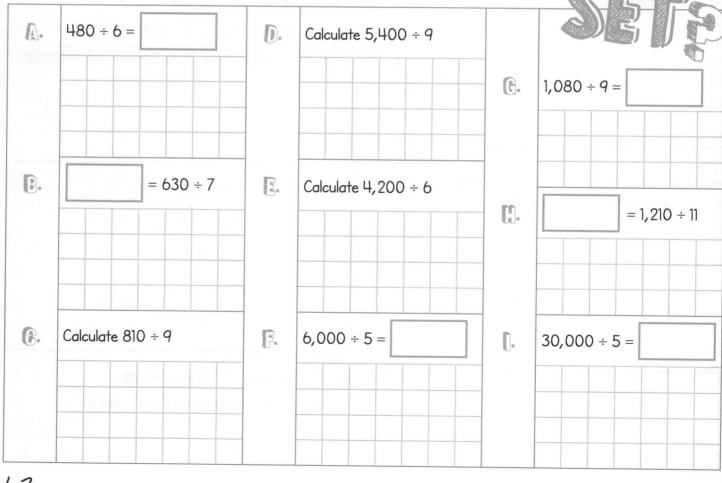

A. $480 ÷ 6 = \boxed{}$

B. $\boxed{} = 630 ÷ 7$

C. Calculate $810 ÷ 9$

D. Calculate $5,400 ÷ 9$

E. Calculate $4,200 ÷ 6$

F. $6,000 ÷ 5 = \boxed{}$

G. $1,080 ÷ 9 = \boxed{}$

H. $\boxed{} = 1,210 ÷ 11$

I. $30,000 ÷ 5 = \boxed{}$

GO!

MENTAL DIVISION

Terrific!

7,200 ÷ 12	1st	Smallest
6,400 ÷ 8	2nd	
4,900 ÷ 7	3rd	
6,000 ÷ 6	4th	
8,100 ÷ 9	5th	
5,500 ÷ 11	6th	Largest

1. Place the calculations in order from smallest to largest.

2. Aled writes:

$$4,900 ÷ 7 = 70$$

Do you agree? Explain your answer.

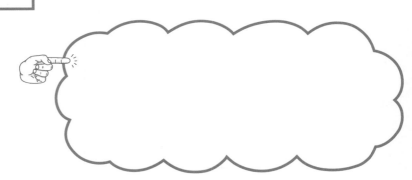

3. There are 840 people playing netball in a national competition.

A netball team has 7 players.

Players can only play for one team.

How many netball teams have entered for the national competition?

4. Always true / Sometimes true / Never true:

The answer to a 3-digit number divided by a 1-digit number has three digits

Explain your answer.

5. Xavier buys a bike that costs £1,320

To pay for the bike he pays the same amount each month for one year.

How much does Xavier pay each month?

The written method of multiplication can be more efficient than partitioning or repeated addition.

For example, 213×3

Partitioning

	200	10	3
3	600	30	9

$600 + 30 + 9 = 639$

Repeated addition

	2	1	3
	2	1	3
+	2	1	3
	6	3	9

The written method of multiplication

H	T	O
2	1	3
×		3
6	3	9

It is important to be confident using the written method with 1-digit numbers before progressing to multiplying by 2-digit numbers.

e.g. 1   Calculate 321×3

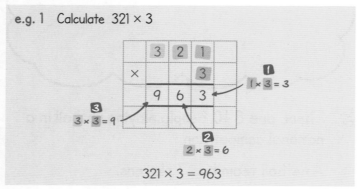

$321 \times 3 = 963$

JUSTAROO Airlines

CHECK-IN

1 6 + 7 =   9 + 8 =

2 Partition 456

3 31 x 2 =   40 x 5 =

4 Circle the answer to 26 x 5:

1,030   130   100   133

Ready for take off?

Sometimes we need to be careful with carry digits ...

e.g. 2 [   ] $= 8,214 \times 7$

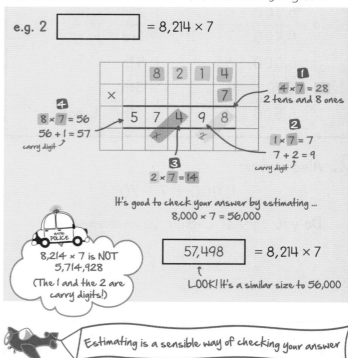

It's good to check your answer by estimating ...
$8,000 \times 7 = 56,000$

8,214 × 7 is NOT 5,714,928
(The 1 and the 2 are carry digits!)

[57,498] $= 8,214 \times 7$

LOOK! It's a similar size to 56,000

Estimating is a sensible way of checking your answer

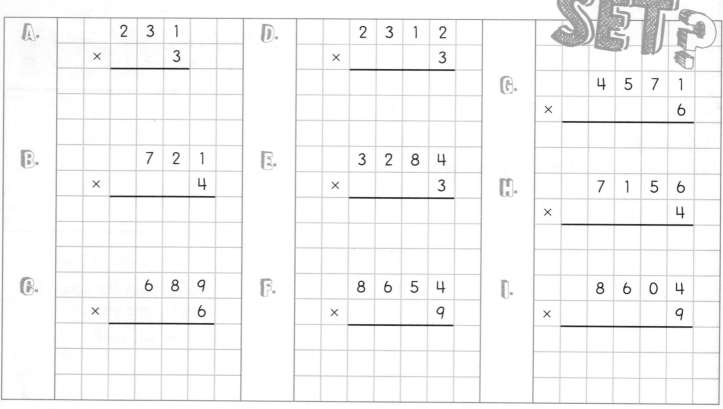

A.

	2	3	1
×			3

B.

	7	2	1
×			4

C.

	6	8	9
×			6

D.

	2	3	1	2
×				3

E.

	3	2	8	4
×				3

F.

	8	6	5	4
×				9

G.

	4	5	7	1
×				6

H.

	7	1	5	6
×				4

I.

	8	6	0	4
×				9

64

GO!

WRITTEN METHODS: MULTIPLICATION 1

1. Find the missing digits.

```
    □   5   0   2
×           □
    _____
□   6   0   1   6
```

2. Becky is calculating 341 × 6

```
        3   4   1
    ×           6
    _____
    1   8   2   4   6
```

Do you agree? Explain your answer.

3. John's challenge is to walk 1,000 km in one year. He plans to walk 3 km every day.

Will he walk at least 1,000 km in one year?

Explain your answer.

4. Find the missing number.

$$\boxed{} \div 9 = 526$$

5. Grandma Lizzie wins some money.

She gives all of the money to her 6 grandchildren.

Each grandchild receives £1,245

How much money did Grandma Lizzie win in total?

£

READY?

When we move on to multiplying a 2-digit number by another 2-digit number we could use the grid method ...

e.g. 31×23

The 'grid method'

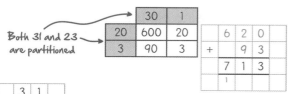

Both 31 and 23 are partitioned

	30	1
20	600	20
3	90	3

	6	2	0
+		9	3
	7	1	3
		1	

		3	1
×		2	3
		9	3
+	6	2	0
	7	1	3
		1	

... but the **written method** of multiplication is more efficient than the grid method, especially for larger numbers.

It is important to be confident using the written method with 2-digit numbers before progressing to multiplying 3 and 4-digit numbers.

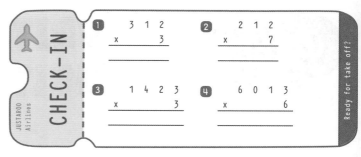

CHECK-IN

1		3	1	2
	×			3

2		2	1	2
	×			7

3		1	4	2	3
	×				3

4		6	0	1	3
	×				6

Sometimes we need to be careful with carry digits ...

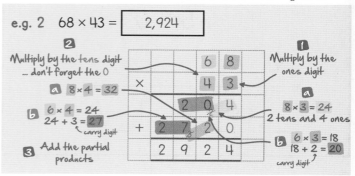

e.g. 2 $68 \times 43 = \boxed{2,924}$

2 Multiply by the tens digit ... don't forget the 0
a $8 \times 4 = 32$
b $6 \times 4 = 24$
$24 + 3 = 27$ ← carry digit
3 Add the partial products

1 Multiply by the ones digit
a $8 \times 3 = 24$
2 tens and 4 ones
b $6 \times 3 = 18$
$18 + 2 = 20$ ← carry digit

		6	8
×		4	3
	2	0	4
+	2	7	2	0
	2	9	2	4

This method can also be used to multiply larger numbers:

e.g. 3 Work out $2,703 \times 87$

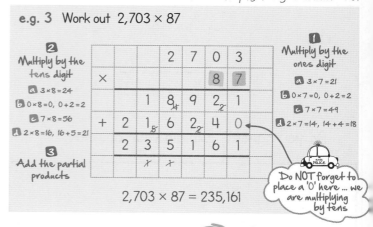

2 Multiply by the tens digit
a $3 \times 8 = 24$
b $0 \times 8 = 0, \ 0 + 2 = 2$
c $7 \times 8 = 56$
d $2 \times 8 = 16, \ 16 + 5 = 21$
3 Add the partial products

1 Multiply by the ones digit
a $3 \times 7 = 21$
b $0 \times 7 = 0, \ 0 + 2 = 2$
c $7 \times 7 = 49$
d $2 \times 7 = 14, \ 14 + 4 = 18$

		2	7	0	3
×			8	7
	1	8	9	2	1
+	2	1	6	2	4	0
	2	3	5	1	6	1

$2,703 \times 87 = 235,161$

Do NOT forget to place a '0' here ... we are multiplying by tens

e.g. 1 Work out 32×21

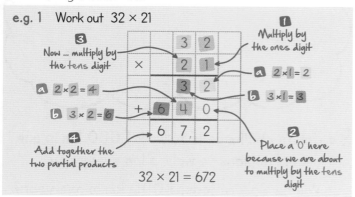

3 Now ... multiply by the tens digit
a $2 \times 2 = 4$
b $3 \times 2 = 6$
4 Add together the two partial products

1 Multiply by the ones digit
a $2 \times 1 = 2$
b $3 \times 1 = 3$

2 Place a '0' here because we are about to multiply by the tens digit

		3	2
×		2	1
		3	2
+	6	4	0
	6	7	2

$32 \times 21 = 672$

SET

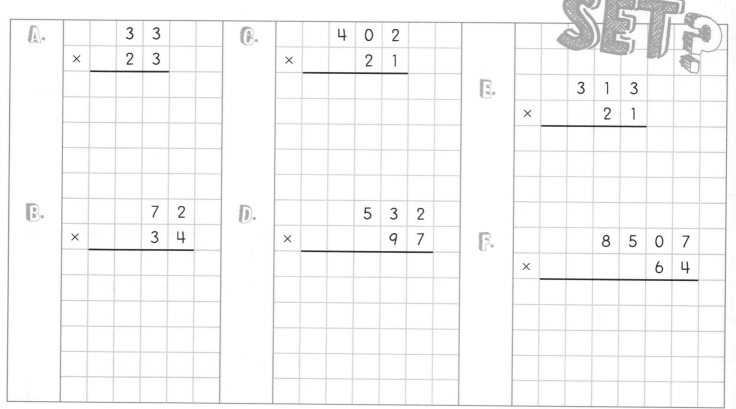

A.

		3	3
×		2	3

B.

		7	2
×		3	4

C.

	4	0	2
×		2	1

D.

	5	3	2
×		9	7

E.

	3	1	3
×		2	1

F.

	8	5	0	7
×			6	4

1. Dee is calculating 67×43

		6	7
×		4	3
	2	0	1
	2	6	8
	4	6	9

Do you agree? Explain your answer.

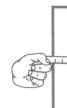

2. A jar holds 124 sweets.

Seth has 2,000 sweets and 17 jars.

Has Seth got enough jars to store all the sweets? Explain your answer.

3. Find the missing number.

$$\boxed{} \div 2{,}163 = 17$$

4. Gary buys a packet of crisps every week.

The crisps cost 75p per packet.

How much does he spend in one year?

£

The written method of division is an efficient way of dividing larger numbers: e.g. $693 \div 3$ ← divisor = 3

dividend = 693

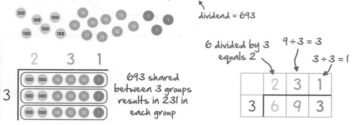

231

693 shared between 3 groups results in 231 in each group

6 divided by 3 equals 2 $9 \div 3 = 3$ $3 \div 3 = 1$

	2	3	1
3	6	9	3

It is important to be confident using the written method with 1-digit numbers before progressing to dividing by 2-digit numbers.

e.g. 1 Calculate $654 \div 3$

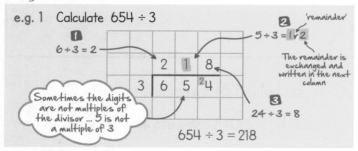

1 $6 \div 3 = 2$

2 'remainder' $5 \div 3 = 1 r 2$

The remainder is exchanged and written in the next column

	2	1	8
3	6	5	^{2}4

Sometimes the digits are not multiples of the divisor ... 5 is not a multiple of 3

3 $24 \div 3 = 8$

$654 \div 3 = 218$

e.g. 2 Work out $984 \div 6$

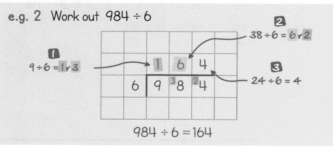

2 $38 \div 6 = 6 r 2$

1 $9 \div 6 = 1 r 3$

	1	6	4
6	9	^{3}8	^{2}4

3 $24 \div 6 = 4$

$984 \div 6 = 164$

CHECK-IN

JUSTAROO Airlines

Ready for take off?

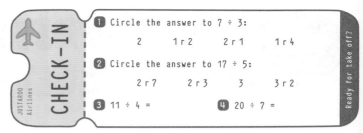

1 Circle the answer to $7 \div 3$:

2   1 r 2   2 r 1   1 r 4

2 Circle the answer to $17 \div 5$:

2 r 7   2 r 3   3   3 r 2

3 $11 \div 4 =$ 4 $20 \div 7 =$

Sometimes the first digit is not a multiple of the divisor.

e.g. 3 Work out $3,595 \div 5$

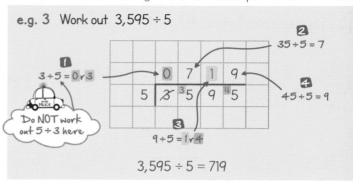

2 $35 \div 5 = 7$

1 $3 \div 5 = 0 r 3$

	0	7	1	9
5	$\cancel{3}$	^{3}5	9	^{4}5

4 $45 \div 5 = 9$

Do NOT work out $5 \div 3$ here

3 $9 \div 5 = 1 r 4$

$3,595 \div 5 = 719$

There could be one or more zeros in the dividend ...

e.g. 4 Work out $8,406 \div 6$

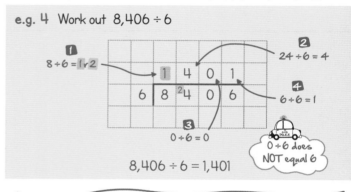

2 $24 \div 6 = 4$

1 $8 \div 6 = 1 r 2$

	1	4	0	1
6	8	^{2}4	0	6

4 $6 \div 6 = 1$

3 $0 \div 6 = 0$

$0 \div 6$ does NOT equal 6

$8,406 \div 6 = 1,401$

The result of a division is called the **quotient**

SET?

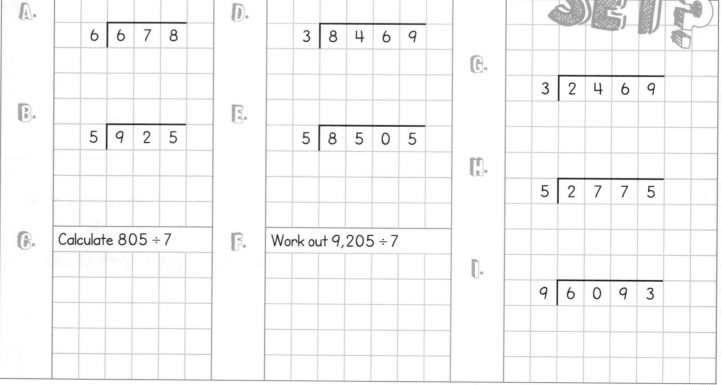

A.

	6	7	8
6			

B.

	9	2	5
5			

C. Calculate $805 \div 7$

D.

	8	4	6	9
3				

E.

	8	5	0	5
5				

F. Work out $9,205 \div 7$

G.

	2	4	6	9
3				

H.

	2	7	7	5
5				

I.

	6	0	9	3
9				

68

1. Find the missing number.

738 ÷ ☐ = 6

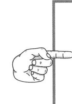

2. Darren writes:

		2	0	1	
3	8	0	4		

Do you agree? Explain your answer.

3. Find the missing digits.

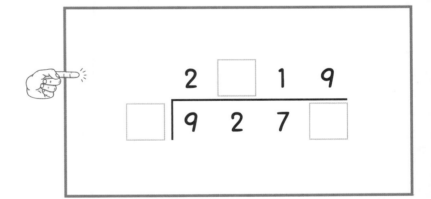

$$2\ \square\ 1\ 9$$
$$\square\ )\ 9\ 2\ 7\ \square$$

4. 470 eggs are placed in boxes of 6 eggs each.

How many boxes are completely filled?

How many eggs are left over?

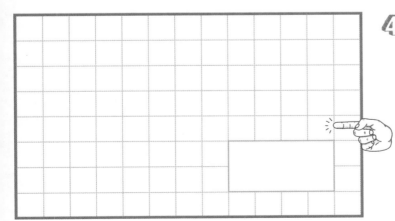

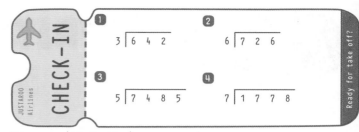

1 $3\overline{)642}$ **2** $6\overline{)726}$

3 $5\overline{)7485}$ **4** $7\overline{)1778}$

The written method of division can also be used to divide by a 2-digit number (or even bigger!)

It can be very helpful to jot a 'multiples of the divisor' table to help, for example: $870 \div 15$

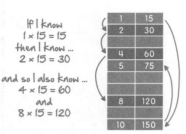

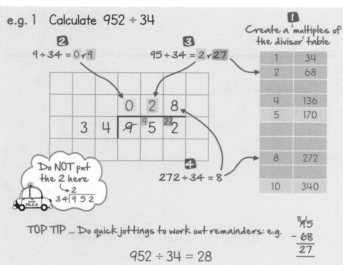

If I know
$1 \times 15 = 15$
then I know ...
$2 \times 15 = 30$

and so I also know ...
$4 \times 15 = 60$
and
$8 \times 15 = 120$

1	15
2	30
4	60
5	75
8	120
10	150

If I know
$1 \times 15 = 15$
then I know ...
$10 \times 15 = 150$

If I know
$10 \times 15 = 150$
then I know ...
$5 \times 15 = 75$

		0	5	8
1	5	$8\,^8 7\,^{12}0$		

So ...
$870 \div 15 = 58$

e.g. 1 Calculate $952 \div 34$

1 Create a 'multiples of the divisor' table

2 $9 \div 34 = 0 \text{ r } 9$

3 $95 \div 34 = 2 \text{ r } 27$

```
        0   2   8
  3  4 | 9  9 5 27 2
```

4 $272 \div 34 = 8$

1	34
2	68
4	136
5	170
8	272
10	340

Do NOT put the 2 here
$\to \frac{2}{34\overline{)952}}$

TOP TIP ... Do quick jottings to work out remainders: e.g.
$\begin{array}{r} ^8 9\,5 \\ -\,6\,8 \\ \hline 2\,7 \end{array}$

$952 \div 34 = 28$

We can also divide larger numbers ...

e.g. 2 Work out $6,834 \div 51$

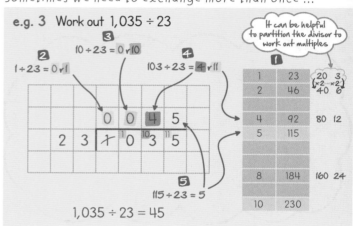

1
| 1 | 51 |
| 2 | 102 |
| 3 | 153 | $102 + 51 = 153$
4	204
5	255
8	408
10	510

2 $6 \div 51 = 0 \text{ r } 6$

3 $68 \div 51 = 1 \text{ r } 17$

4 $173 \div 51 = 3 \text{ r } 20$

```
        0   1   3   4
  5  1 | 6  6 8 17 3 20 4
```

$6,834 \div 51 = 134$ **5** $204 \div 51 = 4$

Sometimes we need to exchange more than once ...

e.g. 3 Work out $1,035 \div 23$

It can be helpful to partition the divisor to work out multiples

1
1	23	20 3 (×2 ×2)
2	46	40 6
4	92	80 12
5	115	
8	184	160 24
10	230	

2 $1 \div 23 = 0 \text{ r } 1$

3 $10 \div 23 = 0 \text{ r } 10$

4 $103 \div 23 = 4 \text{ r } 11$

```
        0   0   4   5
  2  3 | 1  1 0 10 3 11 5
```

5 $115 \div 23 = 5$

$1,035 \div 23 = 45$

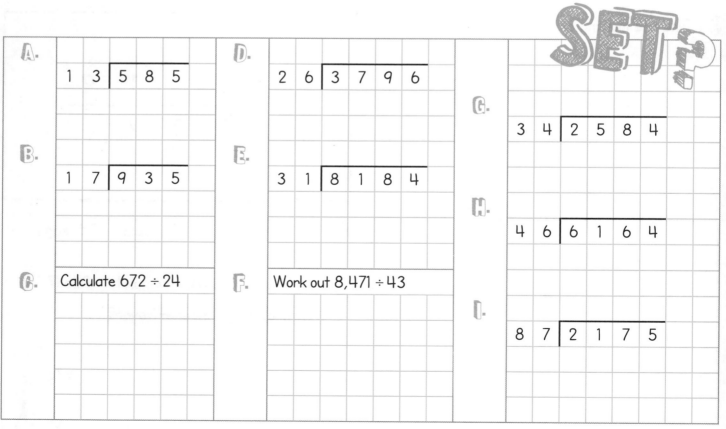

SET?

A. $13\overline{)5\,8\,5}$

B. $17\overline{)9\,3\,5}$

C. Calculate $672 \div 24$

D. $26\overline{)3\,7\,9\,6}$

E. $31\overline{)8\,1\,8\,4}$

F. Work out $8,471 \div 43$

G. $34\overline{)2\,5\,8\,4}$

H. $46\overline{)6\,1\,6\,4}$

I. $87\overline{)2\,1\,7\,5}$

GO!

WRITTEN METHODS: DIVISION 2

1. All pupils and staff at a school are going on a trip.

There are 1,400 pupils and 104 staff.

A coach holds 54 passengers.

Calculate the minimum number of coaches needed.

2. Find the missing number.

$$414 \div \boxed{} = 23$$

3. Laura writes:

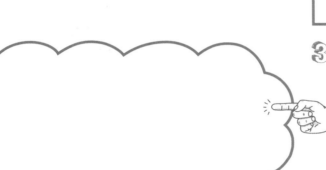

Do you agree? Explain your answer.

4. Always true / Sometimes true / Never true:

The quotient of a 4-digit number and a 2-digit number is a 2-digit number

Explain your answer.

5. Explain how to use $164 \times 16 = 2,624$ to calculate $2,624 \div 32$

READY?

Decimal numbers can be added together using a mental or written method. The written method for adding decimal numbers is the same as for adding whole numbers, but this time we have decimal points ... we must remember to line up the decimal points.

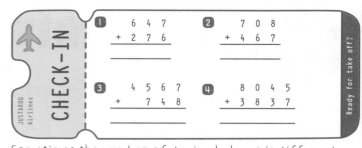

CHECK-IN

JUSTAROO Airlines

Ready for take off?

| ① | 6 4 7 |
| | + 2 7 6 |

| ② | 7 0 8 |
| | + 4 6 7 |

| ③ | 4 5 6 7 |
| | + 7 4 8 |

| ④ | 8 0 4 5 |
| | + 3 8 3 7 |

e.g. 1

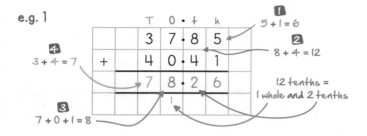

Sometimes we need to be careful with the carry digit ...

e.g. 2

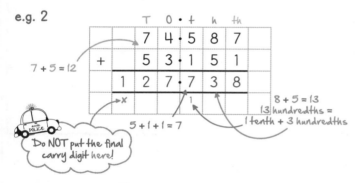

Always check that the decimal points are lined up

Sometimes the number of decimal places is different ...

e.g. 3 Work out 6.7 + 2.869

Be careful to line up tenths with tenths, hundredths with hundredths and so on ... (line up the decimal points)

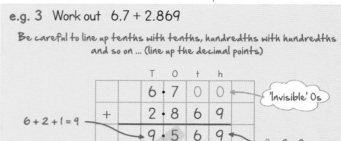

6.7 + 2.869 = 9.569

e.g. 4 ☐ = 96.7 + 8.95

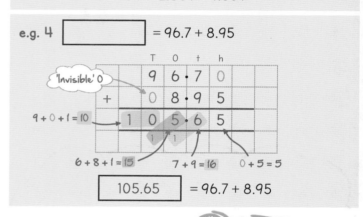

105.65 = 96.7 + 8.95

SET?

| A. | | 6 | 3 . | 2 | 6 |
| | + | 1 | 2 . | 9 | 3 |

| D. | 8.6 + 7.485 = |

| B. | | 6 . | 9 | 0 | 7 |
| | + | 4 . | 6 | 8 | 3 |

| C. | | 7 | 8 . | 9 |
| | + | 4 | 7 . | 8 | 9 |

| E. | ☐ = 17.3 + 7.816 |

GO!

ADDING DECIMALS

Great!

1. Circle the two numbers which sum to 20

| 1.01 | 19.09 | 10.1 | 18.99 | 9.99 |

2. Iliana buys a coat for £78.64 and a dress for £45.99

How much money does Iliana spend altogether?

£ _____

3. Find the missing digits.

```
    7 [ ] . 3  5
 +  [ ]   4 . [ ] [ ]
 ─────────────────
 [ ]  1  6 . 7  9
```

4. Tomas thinks the sum of 23.417 and 5.26 is 23.943

Here is his working:

```
    2 3 · 4 1 7
 +      5 · 2 6
 ──────────────
    2 3 · 9 4 3
            1
```

Explain why Tomas is not correct.

5. The table shows how far Tyrese cycles over three days:

Day	Distance (km)
Monday	8.6
Tuesday	20
Wednesday	15.75

How far does Tyrese cycle in total?

km

READY?

We can subtract decimal numbers using the same written method as for subtracting whole numbers. Again ... we must remember to line up the decimal points.

e.g. 1

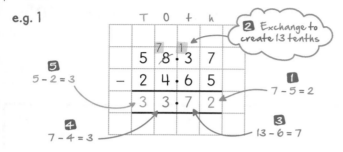

T O t h

$5\ 8 \cdot 3\ 7$ (with small 7 and 1 above)
$-\ 2\ 4 \cdot 6\ 5$
$3\ 3 \cdot 7\ 2$

5 5 – 2 = 3

2 Exchange to create 13 tenths

1 7 – 5 = 2

4 7 – 4 = 3

3 13 – 6 = 7

Be really careful when there are a different number of digits. We use zeros as placeholders.

e.g. 2 Work out 74.918 – 31.62

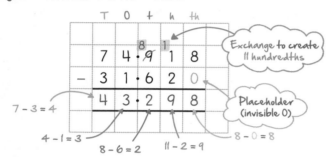

T O t h th

$7\ 4 \cdot 9\ 1\ 8$ (with small 8 and 1 above)
$-\ 3\ 1 \cdot 6\ 2\ 0$
$4\ 3 \cdot 2\ 9\ 8$

7 – 3 = 4

4 – 1 = 3

8 – 6 = 2

11 – 2 = 9

Exchange to create 11 hundredths

Placeholder (invisible 0)

8 – 0 = 8

The result of a subtraction is called a difference

1
$5\ 3\ 4$
$-\ 2\ 7\ 1$

2
$7\ 0\ 6$
$-\ 4\ 8\ 7$

3
$1\ 2\ 0\ 4$
$-\quad 6\ 7\ 8$

4
$3\ 7\ 5\ 2$
$-\ 2\ 8\ 3\ 7$

Be extra careful when the subtrahend (the number being subtracted) has more decimal places than the minuend (the starting number) ...

e.g. 3 Work out 5.7 – 1.43

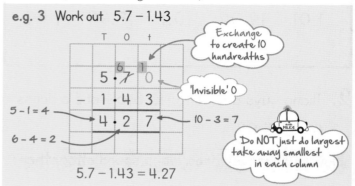

T O t

$5 \cdot 7\ 0$ (with small 6 and 1 above)
$-\ 1 \cdot 4\ 3$
$4 \cdot 2\ 7$

5 – 1 = 4

6 – 4 = 2

Exchange to create 10 hundredths

'Invisible' 0

10 – 3 = 7

$5.7 – 1.43 = 4.27$

Do NOT just do largest take away smallest in each column

We may need to exchange twice (or more) in a row:

e.g. 4 Calculate 5.02 – 1.763

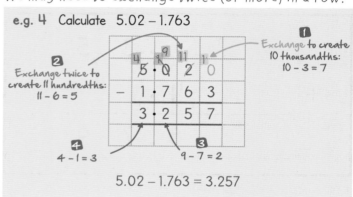

$5 \cdot 0\ 2\ 0$ (with small 4, 9, 11, 1 above)
$-\ 1 \cdot 7\ 6\ 3$
$3 \cdot 2\ 5\ 7$

2 Exchange twice to create 11 hundredths: 11 – 6 = 5

1 Exchange to create 10 thousandths: 10 – 3 = 7

4 4 – 1 = 3

3 9 – 7 = 2

$5.02 – 1.763 = 3.257$

SET?

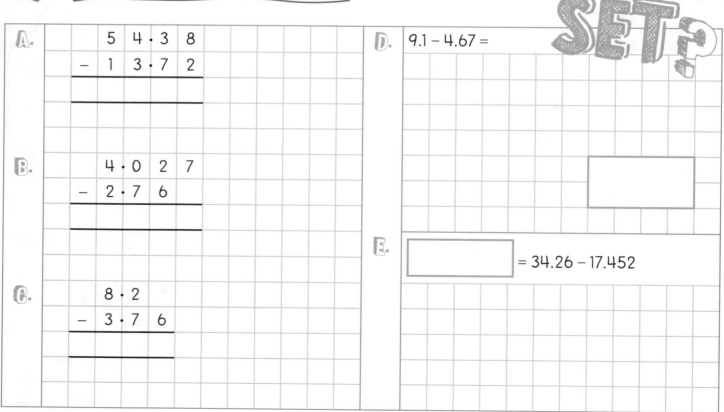

A.

$5\ 4 \cdot 3\ 8$
$-\ 1\ 3 \cdot 7\ 2$

B.

$4 \cdot 0\ 2\ 7$
$-\ 2 \cdot 7\ 6$

C.

$8 \cdot 2$
$-\ 3 \cdot 7\ 6$

D. 9.1 – 4.67 =

E. [   ] = 34.26 – 17.452

GO!

SUBTRACTING DECIMALS

1. The table shows the distances run by Bill and Jill last week.

	Distance (km)
Bill	9.75
Jill	17.235

How much further did Jill run than Bill?

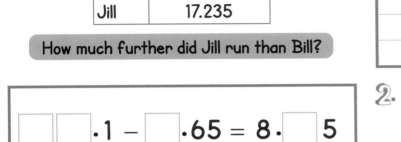

km

2. Use the digits 1, 2, 3 and 4 to complete the calculation.

$$\boxed{}\,\boxed{} \cdot 1 - \boxed{} \cdot 65 = 8 \cdot \boxed{}\, 5$$

HINT: Rewrite using columns?

3. Evie thinks the difference between 28.4 and 15.716 is 12.516

Here is her working:

```
     7
  2  8 · 4
- 1 5 · 7 1 6
  1 2 · 5 1 6
```

Evie is not correct. Explain why.

4. Martin and Janet are raising money for charity.

Martin has raised £46.78

Janet has raised £87.17

How much more money do they need to raise £200?

£

READY?

Decimals can be multiplied by whole numbers using our knowledge of place value and multiplying whole numbers together.

For example, we can compare the answers for the calculations 2×3 and 0.2×3 ...

$$2 \times 3 = 6 \qquad\qquad 0.2 \times 3 = 0.6$$

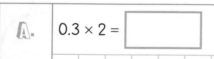

The answer to 0.2×3 is 10 times smaller than the answer to 2×3 ... so if $2 \times 3 = 6$

then $0.2 \times 3 = 0.6$ ◄ 10 times smaller than 6 is the same as $6 \div 10$

e.g. 1 $0.2 \times 4 = \boxed{}$

We know $2 \times 4 = 8$ ...

so 0.2×4 will be 10 times smaller than 2×4

$8 \div 10 = 0.8$

so $0.2 \times 4 = 0.8$

$0.2 \times 4 = \boxed{0.8}$

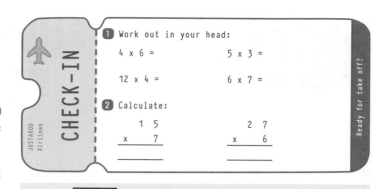

1 Work out in your head:

$4 \times 6 =$ $5 \times 3 =$

$12 \times 4 =$ $6 \times 7 =$

2 Calculate:

$$\begin{array}{r} 1\ 5 \\ \times\ \ 7 \\ \hline \end{array} \qquad\qquad \begin{array}{r} 2\ 7 \\ \times\ \ 6 \\ \hline \end{array}$$

e.g. 2 $\boxed{} = 0.6 \times 8$

0.6×8 will be 10 times smaller than $6 \times 8 = 48$

$0.6 \times 8 = 48 \div 10 = 4.8$

$\boxed{4.8} = 0.6 \times 8$

 0.6×8 does NOT equal 0.48

e.g. 3   Calculate 1.2×3

$\div 10 \left(\begin{array}{l} 12 \times 3 = 36 \\ 1.2 \times 3 = 3.6 \end{array} \right) \div 10$

We can choose either a mental or written method to help with the calculation ...

e.g. 4   Work out 2.6×3

1 Work out 26×3

$$\begin{array}{r} 26 \\ \times\ 3 \\ \hline 78 \\ {\scriptstyle 1} \end{array}$$ **OR**

$20 \times 3 = 60$
$6 \times 3 = 18$
$26 \times 3 = 60 + 18 = 78$

2

$\div 10 \left(\begin{array}{l} 26 \times 3 = 78 \\ 2.6 \times 3 = 7.8 \end{array} \right) \div 10$

SET?

A. $0.3 \times 2 = \boxed{}$

B. $\boxed{} = 0.5 \times 3$

C.   Calculate 0.4×6

D.   Calculate 1.2×4

E. $1.5 \times 7 = \boxed{}$

F. $\boxed{} = 2.7 \times 6$

GO!

MULTIPLICATION WITH DECIMALS

1. Find the missing number:

$$6 \times \boxed{} = 3$$

2. Neve writes:

$$0.7 \times 9 = 0.63$$

Do you agree? Explain your answer.

3. A packet of crisps costs £0.40

Ed buys 9 packets.

He pays with a £5 note.

How much change does Ed get?

£

4. Harry is pouring lemonade into some cups.

He has a $2\frac{1}{2}$ litre bottle of lemonade.

He pours 0.3 litres of lemonade into each cup.

Harry fills 7 cups, how much lemonade is left in the bottle?

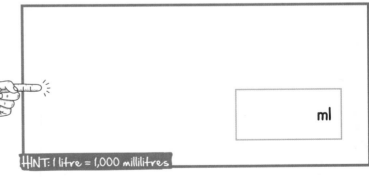

ml

HINT: 1 litre = 1,000 millilitres

5. Place the calculations in order from largest to smallest product.

1.4 × 4	1st	Largest
0.6 × 7	2nd	
9 × 0.5	3rd	
2.4 × 2	4th	
0.7 × 7	5th	Smallest

READY?

Different fractions can be used to describe the same shaded section in these rectangles:

The shaded section is one of two equal parts. So it is $\frac{1}{2}$ of the rectangle.

| 1 | 2 | | |

The same section is also two of four equal parts. So it is $\frac{2}{4}$ of the rectangle.

| 1 | 2 |
| 3 | 4 |

It could also be seen as four of eight equal parts. So it is $\frac{4}{8}$ of the rectangle.

These fractions are known as equivalent fractions. For every fraction, there is a family of equivalent fractions: e.g.

$$\overset{\times 2 \quad \times 2}{\frac{1}{2} = \frac{2}{4} = \frac{4}{8}}_{\times 2 \quad \times 2}$$

e.g. 1 Find three different fractions that are equivalent to $\frac{1}{5}$

We need to multiply the numerator and denominator by the same number ... we can pick ANY number

$$\overset{\times 2}{\underset{\times 2}{\frac{1}{5} = \frac{2}{10}}} \qquad \overset{\times 3}{\underset{\times 3}{\frac{1}{5} = \frac{3}{15}}} \qquad \overset{\times 4}{\underset{\times 4}{\frac{1}{5} = \frac{4}{20}}}$$

Three fractions that are equivalent to $\frac{1}{5}$ are $\frac{2}{10}$, $\frac{3}{15}$ and $\frac{4}{20}$

Sometimes we know the denominator ...

e.g. 2 Find the missing number: $\frac{1}{2} = \frac{\square}{10}$

1. Use multiplication facts to solve $2 \times ? = 10$ $\overset{}{\frac{1}{2} = \frac{\square}{10}}$

$$\overset{\times 5}{\frac{1}{2}} = \frac{\boxed{5}}{10}$$ 2. Multiply the numerator by the same number

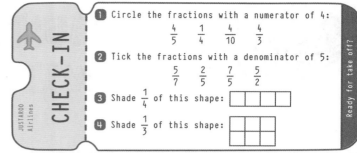
JUSTAROO Airlines CHECK-IN

1. Circle the fractions with a numerator of 4:
$\frac{4}{5}$ $\frac{1}{4}$ $\frac{4}{10}$ $\frac{4}{3}$

2. Tick the fractions with a denominator of 5:
$\frac{5}{7}$ $\frac{2}{5}$ $\frac{7}{5}$ $\frac{5}{2}$

3. Shade $\frac{1}{4}$ of this shape:

4. Shade $\frac{1}{3}$ of this shape:

Ready for take off?

... and sometimes the numerator:

e.g. 3 Find the missing number: $\frac{3}{\square} = \frac{9}{12}$

 1. $\frac{3}{\square} = \frac{9}{12}$

 2. $\overset{}{\underset{\div 3}{\frac{3}{4} = \frac{9}{12}}}$

We could also use a table to help instead

$\div 3$	
3	9
4	12

$\div 3$

We use equivalent fractions to help order fractions:

e.g. 4 Place the fractions in order from smallest to largest:

$$\frac{1}{3}, \frac{5}{6}, \frac{4}{9}, \frac{7}{12}$$

1. Look for any fractions that are less than one half $\frac{1}{3}$ and $\frac{4}{9}$

2. Use equivalent fractions to compare $\frac{1}{3}$ and $\frac{4}{9}$ $\overset{\times 3}{\underset{\times 3}{\frac{1}{3} = \frac{3}{9}}}$ so $\frac{1}{3}$ is less than $\frac{4}{9}$

3. Use equivalent fractions to compare $\frac{5}{6}$ and $\frac{7}{12}$ $\overset{\times 2}{\underset{\times 2}{\frac{5}{6} = \frac{10}{12}}}$ so $\frac{7}{12}$ is less than $\frac{5}{6}$

4. Write all the fractions in order $\frac{1}{3}, \frac{4}{9}, \frac{7}{12}, \frac{5}{6}$

OR

We could write all the fractions with a common denominator of 36 ...

$$\frac{1}{3} = \frac{12}{36} \qquad \frac{5}{6} = \frac{30}{36} \qquad \frac{4}{9} = \frac{16}{36} \qquad \frac{7}{12} = \frac{21}{36}$$ ... then order by numerator

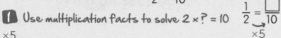

A. Find three different equivalent fractions to describe the shaded section of the diagram:

| | | | | | |
| | | | | | |

B. Find the missing numbers:

(i) $\frac{1}{2} = \frac{\square}{6}$

(ii) $\frac{1}{3} = \frac{\square}{6}$

(iii) $\frac{1}{5} = \frac{\square}{500}$

C. Find the missing numbers:

(i) $\frac{2}{\square} = \frac{8}{12}$

(ii) $\frac{3}{5} = \frac{24}{\square}$

(iii) $\frac{3}{\square} = \frac{150}{400}$

D. Place the fractions in order from smallest to largest:

$$\frac{1}{2}, \frac{3}{8}, \frac{3}{4}, \frac{7}{16}$$

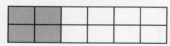

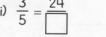

SET?

E. Place the fractions in order from largest to smallest:

$$\frac{9}{20}, \frac{2}{5}, \frac{8}{15}, \frac{5}{10}$$

GO! EQUIVALENT FRACTIONS

1. Taylor drinks $\frac{2}{3}$ of a litre of water.

   Tina drinks $\frac{5}{7}$ of a litre of water.

   Who drinks more? Explain your answer.

2. Blake thinks that $\frac{3}{5}$ and $\frac{6}{8}$ are equivalent fractions. He has written:

   $$\overset{+3}{\underset{+3}{\frac{3}{5} = \frac{6}{8}}}$$

   Do you agree? Explain your answer.

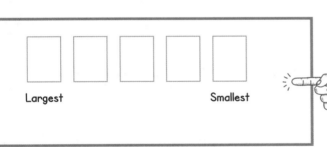

Largest   Smallest

3. Place the fractions in order.

   $\frac{2}{3}$ $\frac{3}{4}$ $\frac{5}{6}$ $\frac{5}{12}$ $\frac{7}{9}$

4. Find the missing digits.

   $$\frac{1 + \boxed{}}{4} = \frac{9}{12} = \frac{27}{30 + \boxed{}}$$

5. Use the digits 1, 2, 3, 4, 6, 8 and 9 to complete the family of equivalent fractions.

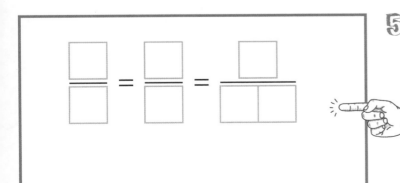

READY?

We can simplify a fraction by dividing both the numerator and denominator by a common factor. A fraction is fully simplified when both the numerator and denominator are the smallest possible values.

For example, we know that $\frac{8}{20}$ and $\frac{2}{5}$ are equivalent fractions:

$\frac{8}{20}$ can be simplified fully to $\frac{2}{5}$ by dividing both the numerator and denominator by their highest common factor ... in this case 4

$$\frac{8}{20} = \frac{2}{5} \quad {\div 4 \atop \div 4}$$

e.g. 1   Simplify fully: $\frac{6}{10}$

1 Find the highest common factor of 6 and 10

Factors of 6 → 1, ②, 3, 6   Factors of 10 → 1, ②, 5, 10

2 Divide both the numerator and denominator by 2

$$\frac{6}{10} = \frac{3}{5} \quad {\div 2 \atop \div 2}$$

Look out for when a fraction can be simplified by dividing by an odd number ...

e.g. 2   Simplify fully: $\frac{9}{12}$

1 Find the HCF of 9 and 12

Factors of 9 → 1, ③, 9
Factors of 12 → 1, 2, ③, 4, 6, 12

2 Divide ...

$$\frac{9}{12} = \frac{3}{4} \quad {\div 3 \atop \div 3}$$

CHECK-IN

JUSTAROO Airlines

1 Write down all the factors of 24

2 Circle the factors of 8:

   1   2   4   8   16   24

3 True or false: 30 is a common factor of 5 and 10?

4 Circle the highest common factor of 8 and 12:

   24   2   4   8

Ready for take off?

e.g. 3   Simplify fully: $\frac{15}{20}$

1 Find the HCF of 15 and 20

Factors of 15 → 1, 3, ⑤, 15
Factors of 20 → 1, 2, 4, ⑤, 10, 20

2 Divide ...

$$\frac{15}{20} = \frac{3}{4} \quad {\div 5 \atop \div 5}$$

Dividing by 2 to get $\frac{7.5}{10}$ is NOT simplifying

Sometimes it can be easier to simplify a fraction fully by taking a couple of steps ...

e.g. 4   Simplify fully: $\frac{90}{150}$

$$\frac{90}{150} = \frac{9}{15} \quad {\div 10 \atop \div 10}$$

Look ... 10 is a factor of both numerator and denominator

3 is a factor of both 9 and 15, so we can simplify again

$$\frac{9}{15} = \frac{3}{5} \quad {\div 3 \atop \div 3}$$

We could have simplified in one step by dividing by 30

So $\frac{90}{150} = \frac{3}{5}$

A fraction can be simplified by dividing both top and bottom by their highest common factor

---

A. Tick the fractions that can be simplified.

$\frac{4}{9}$ ☐ $\frac{9}{19}$ ☐

$\frac{5}{15}$ ☐ $\frac{14}{21}$ ☐

$\frac{3}{12}$ ☐ $\frac{7}{50}$ ☐

$\frac{8}{18}$ ☐ $\frac{25}{100}$ ☐

C. Simplify fully:

(i) $\frac{8}{24}$ (iii) $\frac{12}{80}$

(ii) $\frac{6}{30}$ (iv) $\frac{40}{48}$

B. Tick the fractions that are not in their simplest form. Write these fractions in their simplest form.

$\frac{3}{9}$ ☐ $\frac{9}{25}$ ☐

$\frac{4}{15}$ ☐ $\frac{16}{40}$ ☐

$\frac{8}{20}$ ☐ $\frac{11}{50}$ ☐

SET?

D. Simplify fully:

(i) $\frac{25}{100}$

(ii) $\frac{60}{150}$

(iii) $\frac{80}{200}$

(iv) $\frac{150}{500}$

SIMPLIFYING FRACTIONS

1. Always true / Sometimes true / Never true:

> To simplify a fraction, you keep halving the numerator and denominator until you can't halve them anymore

Explain your answer.

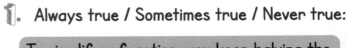

2. Amy crosses out the twos to simplify the fraction $\frac{12}{26}$

$$\frac{12}{26} = \frac{1}{6}$$

Explain why Amy is not correct.

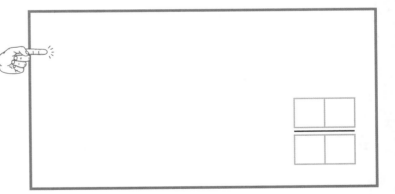

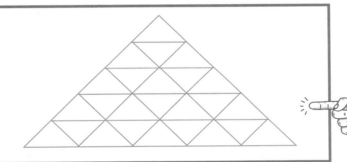

3. Shade $\frac{3}{5}$ of the diagram.

4. Gemma simplifies a fraction to $\frac{3}{8}$

The numerator and the denominator both have two digits.

The digits of the numerator are the same as the digits of the denominator, but in reverse order.

Find Gemma's fraction.

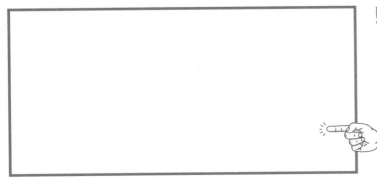

5. Benita has completed a test with 40 questions.

She gets more than $\frac{3}{5}$ but less than $\frac{3}{4}$ of the questions correct.

What is the maximum number of questions Benita could have answered correctly?

A fraction which has a numerator less than the denominator is called a **proper fraction**:

e.g. $\frac{1}{2}$, $\frac{2}{3}$ and $\frac{5}{7}$ etc.

A fraction with a numerator greater than or equal to the denominator is called an **improper fraction**:

e.g. $\frac{3}{2}$, $\frac{5}{3}$ and $\frac{9}{9}$ etc.

An improper fraction can also be written as a **mixed number**.

 $\frac{5}{3} = 1\frac{2}{3}$

A mixed number has two parts ... a whole number and a proper fraction.

e.g. 1 Write $\frac{7}{4}$ as a mixed number

Remember:
$\frac{4}{4} = 1$ whole

7 quarters is 7 'one quarters'

1	2	3	4
5	6	7	

$\frac{7}{4} = 1\frac{3}{4}$

Sometimes the whole number is greater than 1.

e.g. 2 Write $\frac{7}{3}$ as a mixed number

$7 \div 3 = 2$ r 1

7 thirds =
2 wholes
+ 1 third left over

1	2	3
4	5	6
7		

2 r 1 is NOT $2\frac{1}{7}$

$\frac{7}{3} = 2\frac{1}{3}$

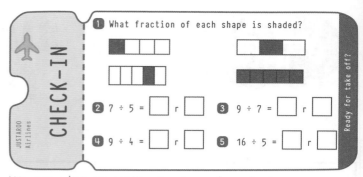

CHECK-IN

JUSTAROO Airlines

Ready for take off?

1 What fraction of each shape is shaded?

2 $7 \div 5 = \boxed{}$ r $\boxed{}$ **3** $9 \div 7 = \boxed{}$ r $\boxed{}$

4 $9 \div 4 = \boxed{}$ r $\boxed{}$ **5** $16 \div 5 = \boxed{}$ r $\boxed{}$

We can also convert mixed numbers to improper fractions ...

e.g. 3 Write $1\frac{4}{5}$ as an improper fraction

$1\frac{4}{5}$ → 1 and $\frac{4}{5}$

1	2	3	4	5
6	7	8	9	

$\frac{5}{5} = 1$ whole

$1 + \frac{4}{5} = \frac{5}{5} + \frac{4}{5} = \frac{9}{5}$

$1\frac{4}{5} = \frac{9}{5}$

We can also convert mixed numbers when the whole number part is greater than 1 ...

e.g. 4 Write $2\frac{1}{6}$ as an improper fraction

$2\frac{1}{6}$

1	2	3	4	5	6
7	8	9	10	11	12
13					

2 wholes = 2 × 6 sixths = 12 sixths

Plus one more sixth
= 13 sixths altogether

$2\frac{1}{6} = \frac{13}{6}$

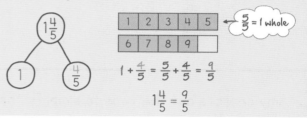
A mixed number has two parts ... a whole number and a proper fraction

---

SET?

A. Write $\frac{7}{5}$ as a mixed number	**D.** Write $\frac{16}{5}$ as a mixed number	**G.** Write $3\frac{1}{2}$ as an improper fraction
B. Write $\frac{9}{7}$ as a mixed number	**E.** Write $1\frac{5}{6}$ as an improper fraction	
C. Write $\frac{9}{4}$ as a mixed number	**F.** Write $2\frac{2}{5}$ as an improper fraction	**H.** Write $4\frac{2}{9}$ as an improper fraction

MIXED NUMBERS

Tekkers!

1. Place the fractions in order, smallest to largest.

$$\frac{11}{8} \qquad \frac{10}{3} \qquad 1\frac{1}{2} \qquad \frac{11}{6}$$

2. Find the missing digits.

$$\frac{\boxed{\,\boxed{}}}{7} = 2\frac{1}{\boxed{}}$$

3. Timmy writes:

$$\frac{8}{5} = 1\frac{3}{8}$$

Explain why Timmy is not correct.

4. Complete the empty boxes so that each mixed number can be matched to its equivalent improper fraction.

Mixed number	Improper fraction
$4\frac{2}{3}$	$\frac{11}{4}$
$5\frac{1}{2}$	$\frac{17}{3}$
$3\frac{2}{3}$	
	$\frac{14}{3}$
$5\frac{2}{3}$	$\frac{11}{3}$

5. Joni has some cakes.

She cuts them into slices. Each slice is one eighth of a cake.

Joni has 24 slices altogether.

How many cakes did Joni start with?

READY?

Fractions can be used to find parts of an amount. It is useful to sketch a bar model.

For example $\frac{1}{5}$ of 20:

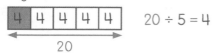

$20 \div 5 = 4$

The **denominator** tells us how many equal parts to <u>divide</u> the amount into (in this case 5). The numerator tells us the <u>number</u> of parts we need (in this case 1).

The amount represents the 'whole' (in this case 20).

It is really helpful to know division facts from the multiplication tables when finding a fraction of an amount.

e.g. 1a Find $\frac{1}{3}$ of 24

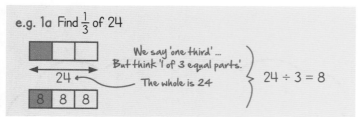

We say 'one third' ... But think '1 of 3 equal parts'. The whole is 24

$24 \div 3 = 8$

The numerator is not always 1 ...

e.g. 1b Find $\frac{2}{3}$ of 24

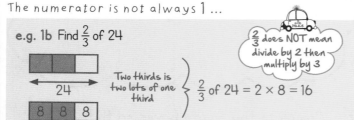

Two thirds is two lots of one third

$\frac{2}{3}$ does NOT mean divide by 2 then multiply by 3

$\frac{2}{3}$ of 24 = 2 × 8 = 16

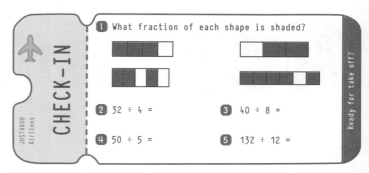

JUSTAROO Airlines **CHECK-IN** Ready for take off?

1 What fraction of each shape is shaded?

2 $32 \div 4 =$

3 $40 \div 8 =$

4 $50 \div 5 =$

5 $132 \div 12 =$

e.g. 2 Find $\frac{3}{5}$ of 30

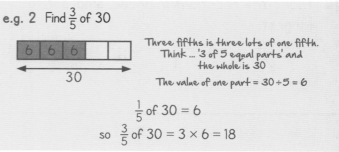

Three fifths is three lots of one fifth. Think ... '3 of 5 equal parts' and the whole is 30

The value of one part = $30 \div 5 = 6$

$\frac{1}{5}$ of 30 = 6

so $\frac{3}{5}$ of 30 = 3 × 6 = 18

We can also solve problems involving multiplication:

e.g. 3 Find $\frac{4}{9} \times 18$

We can read this as $\frac{4}{9}$ of 18

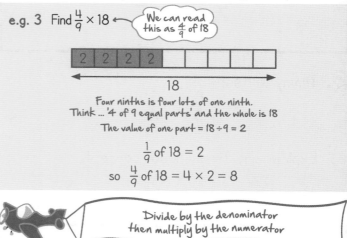

Four ninths is four lots of one ninth. Think ... '4 of 9 equal parts' and the whole is 18

The value of one part = $18 \div 9 = 2$

$\frac{1}{9}$ of 18 = 2

so $\frac{4}{9}$ of 18 = 4 × 2 = 8

Divide by the denominator then multiply by the numerator

SET?

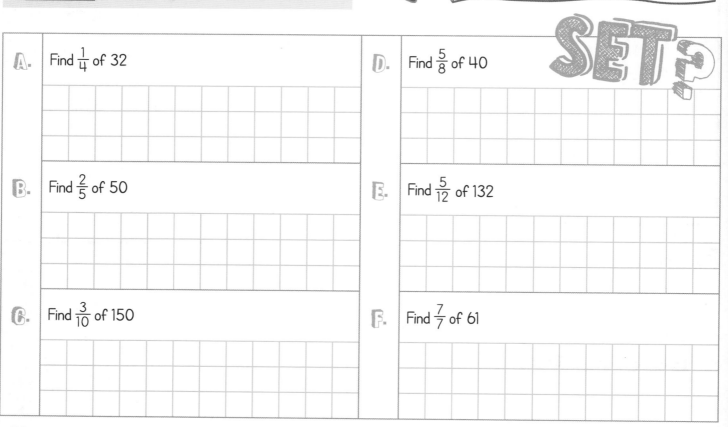

A. Find $\frac{1}{4}$ of 32

B. Find $\frac{2}{5}$ of 50

C. Find $\frac{3}{10}$ of 150

D. Find $\frac{5}{8}$ of 40

E. Find $\frac{5}{12}$ of 132

F. Find $\frac{7}{7}$ of 61

GO!

FRACTION OF AN AMOUNT

1. There are 27 pupils in a class.

One third of the class are boys.

What is the total number of girls in the class?

2. Carol writes:

$$\frac{2}{3} \text{ of } 12 = 18$$

because $12 \div 2 = 6$ and $6 \times 3 = 18$

Do you agree? Explain your answer.

3. Use the digits 0, 1, 2, 4 and 6 to complete the calculation.

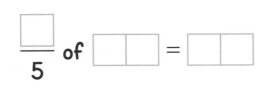

$$\frac{\square}{5} \text{ of } \boxed{} = \boxed{}$$

4. Work out the answers to the calculations.
Match each answer with its order.

$\frac{1}{4}$ of 80	1st	Largest
$\frac{5}{6}$ of 30	2nd	
$\frac{2}{7}$ of 77	3rd	
$\frac{3}{8}$ of 80	4th	
$\frac{4}{5}$ of 30	5th	Smallest

5. $\frac{3}{4}$ of a number is 60

Find the number.

READY?

We can add fractions with the same denominator by using our knowledge of addition:

two badgers add **three** badgers equals **five** badgers

$$20 + 30 = 50$$

two <u>tens</u> add **three** <u>tens</u> equals **five** <u>tens</u>

$$\frac{2}{6} + \frac{3}{6} = \frac{5}{6}$$

two <u>sixths</u> add **three** <u>sixths</u> equals **five** <u>sixths</u>

e.g. 1 $\frac{1}{5} + \frac{2}{5} = \boxed{}$

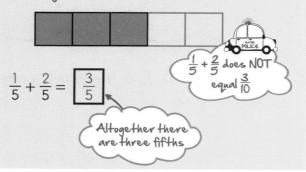

Drawing a bar can be useful ...

$\frac{1}{5} + \frac{2}{5} = \boxed{\frac{3}{5}}$

$\frac{1}{5} + \frac{2}{5}$ does NOT equal $\frac{3}{10}$

Altogether there are three fifths

When adding fractions with the same denominator, add the numerators ... but not the denominators

JUSTAROO Airlines

CHECK-IN

Ready for take off?

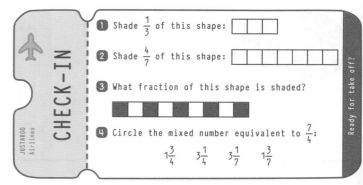

1 Shade $\frac{1}{3}$ of this shape:

2 Shade $\frac{4}{7}$ of this shape:

3 What fraction of this shape is shaded?

4 Circle the mixed number equivalent to $\frac{7}{4}$:

$1\frac{3}{4}$ $3\frac{1}{4}$ $3\frac{1}{7}$ $1\frac{3}{7}$

e.g. 2 $\frac{3}{8} + \frac{2}{8} = \boxed{\frac{5}{8}}$

Altogether, there are five eighths

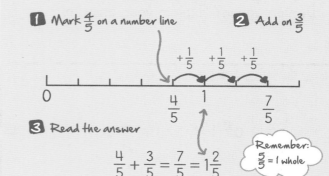

We can also think about adding fractions by counting on a number line.

e.g. 3   Calculate $\frac{4}{5} + \frac{3}{5}$

Give your answer as a mixed number.

1 Mark $\frac{4}{5}$ on a number line   2 Add on $\frac{3}{5}$

$+\frac{1}{5}$ $+\frac{1}{5}$ $+\frac{1}{5}$

0     $\frac{4}{5}$ 1 $\frac{7}{5}$

3 Read the answer

$$\frac{4}{5} + \frac{3}{5} = \frac{7}{5} = 1\frac{2}{5}$$

Remember: $\frac{5}{5} = 1$ whole

SET?

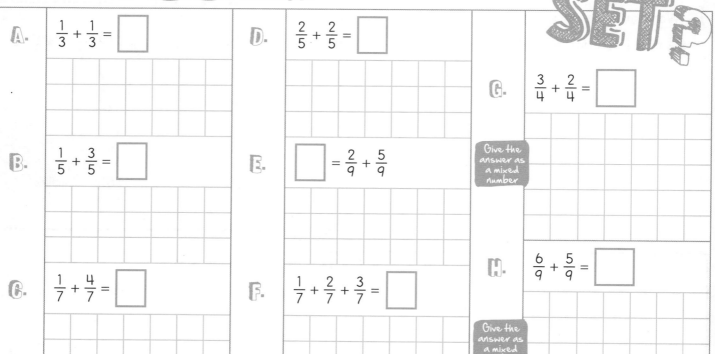

A. $\frac{1}{3} + \frac{1}{3} = \boxed{}$

B. $\frac{1}{5} + \frac{3}{5} = \boxed{}$

C. $\frac{1}{7} + \frac{4}{7} = \boxed{}$

D. $\frac{2}{5} + \frac{2}{5} = \boxed{}$

E. $\boxed{} = \frac{2}{9} + \frac{5}{9}$

F. $\frac{1}{7} + \frac{2}{7} + \frac{3}{7} = \boxed{}$

G. $\frac{3}{4} + \frac{2}{4} = \boxed{}$

Give the answer as a mixed number

H. $\frac{6}{9} + \frac{5}{9} = \boxed{}$

Give the answer as a mixed number

1. Mel and Fize are eating a pizza.

   Mel eats $\frac{1}{8}$ of the pizza.

   Fize eats $\frac{3}{8}$ of the pizza.

   What fraction of the pizza is left?

2. Find the missing digits.

$$\frac{2}{3} + \frac{\square}{3} = \frac{7}{\square}$$

3. Sam thinks that:

$$\frac{1}{6} + \frac{4}{6} = \frac{5}{12}$$

   Explain why Sam is not correct.

4. Write numbers in the empty boxes so that each calculation can be matched with its sum.

$\frac{1}{8} + \frac{6}{8} =$ $1\frac{3}{8}$

$\frac{3}{8} + \frac{1}{8} =$ $\frac{7}{16}$

$\frac{3}{\square} + \frac{\square}{\square} =$ $\frac{4}{8}$

$\frac{5}{8} + \frac{6}{8} =$ $\frac{\square}{\square}$

 **READY?**

We can easily add fractions when the denominators are the same. When the denominators are not the same, we need to use our knowledge of equivalent fractions to find a **common denominator**.

 Ready for take off?

JUSTAROO Airlines

CHECK-IN

1 True or false: $\frac{2}{5} + \frac{1}{5} = \frac{3}{10}$?

2 Circle all the fractions equivalent to $\frac{1}{3}$:
$\frac{2}{6}$ $\frac{2}{4}$ $\frac{3}{9}$ $\frac{1}{9}$

3 Circle all the fractions equivalent to $\frac{3}{5}$:
$\frac{6}{10}$ $\frac{4}{6}$ $\frac{3}{15}$ $\frac{9}{15}$

4 Write $\frac{19}{12}$ as a mixed number

 $\frac{1}{4} + \frac{1}{8}$ is equivalent to $\frac{2}{8} + \frac{1}{8}$

Denominators are not the same

common denominator

because: $\frac{1}{4} = \frac{2}{8}$ (×2)

e.g. 1 $\frac{1}{2} + \frac{1}{4} = \boxed{}$

$\frac{1}{2} + \frac{1}{4}$ does NOT equal $\frac{2}{6}$

Drawing a bar can be useful ...

... but drawing a bar using equivalent fractions is more useful

$\frac{1}{2} + \frac{1}{4} = \frac{2}{4} + \frac{1}{4} = \frac{3}{4}$

Denominators are now the same

$\frac{1}{2} + \frac{1}{4} = \boxed{\frac{3}{4}}$

e.g. 2 $\frac{2}{3} + \frac{2}{9} = \boxed{\frac{8}{9}}$

$\frac{6}{9} + \frac{2}{9} = \frac{8}{9}$

×3
$\frac{2}{3} = \frac{6}{9}$
×3

Sometimes we need to find equivalent fractions for both fractions ...

e.g. 3 Calculate $\frac{3}{4} + \frac{1}{6}$

1 Look for the lowest common multiple of 4 and 6

Multiples of 4 → 4, 8, 12, 16, ...
Multiples of 6 → 6, 12, 18, 24, ...

2 Find equivalent fractions for $\frac{3}{4}$ and $\frac{1}{6}$

×3
$\frac{3}{4} = \frac{9}{12}$
×3

×2
$\frac{1}{6} = \frac{2}{12}$
×2

3 Rewrite the sum using fractions with the common denominator

$\frac{3}{4} + \frac{1}{6} = \frac{9}{12} + \frac{2}{12} = \frac{11}{12}$

 When adding fractions with different denominators, find a **common denominator**

SET?

A. $\frac{1}{3} + \frac{1}{6} = \boxed{}$

B. $\frac{1}{5} + \frac{1}{10} = \boxed{}$

C. $\frac{1}{4} + \frac{1}{8} = \boxed{}$

D. $\frac{3}{5} + \frac{2}{15} = \boxed{}$

E. $\boxed{} = \frac{2}{9} + \frac{2}{3}$

F. $\frac{1}{4} + \frac{1}{2} + \frac{1}{8} = \boxed{}$

G. $\frac{1}{4} + \frac{3}{10} = \boxed{}$

H. $\frac{1}{3} + \frac{1}{4} = \boxed{}$

ADDING FRACTIONS 2

Notable!

1. Joe runs $\frac{3}{4}$ of a kilometre on Monday.

   He runs $\frac{5}{6}$ of a kilometre on Tuesday.

   How far does he run altogether?
   Write your answer as a mixed number.

km

2. Find the missing digits.

$$\frac{1}{3} + \frac{4}{\boxed{}} = \frac{\boxed{}}{9}$$

3. $\frac{1}{2}$ of a flag is blue. $\frac{1}{5}$ of the flag is pink.

   The rest of the flag is orange.

   What fraction of the flag is not orange?

4. Place the calculations in order.

$\frac{1}{4} + \frac{1}{8}$	Largest sum
$\frac{1}{4} + \frac{1}{2}$	
$\frac{1}{2} + \frac{1}{3}$	
$\frac{1}{2} + \frac{1}{6}$	Smallest sum

Mixed numbers and proper fractions can be added together using our knowledge of adding proper fractions.

It is useful to remember that a mixed number has two parts ... a whole number and a proper fraction.

$1\frac{4}{5}$

1 $\frac{4}{5}$

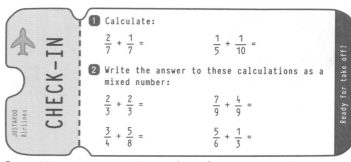

JUSTAROO Airlines   CHECK-IN

1 Calculate:

$\frac{2}{7} + \frac{1}{7} =$ $\frac{1}{5} + \frac{1}{10} =$

2 Write the answer to these calculations as a mixed number:

$\frac{2}{3} + \frac{2}{3} =$ $\frac{7}{9} + \frac{4}{9} =$

$\frac{3}{4} + \frac{5}{8} =$ $\frac{5}{6} + \frac{1}{3} =$

Ready for take off?

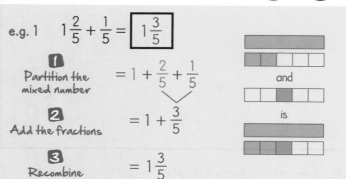

e.g. 1 $1\frac{2}{5} + \frac{1}{5} = \boxed{1\frac{3}{5}}$

1 Partition the mixed number $= 1 + \frac{2}{5} + \frac{1}{5}$

2 Add the fractions $= 1 + \frac{3}{5}$

3 Recombine $= 1\frac{3}{5}$

and

is

We can also add mixed numbers together ...

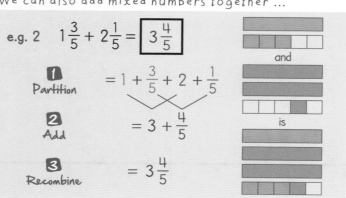

e.g. 2 $1\frac{3}{5} + 2\frac{1}{5} = \boxed{3\frac{4}{5}}$

1 Partition $= 1 + \frac{3}{5} + 2 + \frac{1}{5}$

2 Add $= 3 + \frac{4}{5}$

3 Recombine $= 3\frac{4}{5}$

and

is

Sometimes we need to deal with improper fractions:

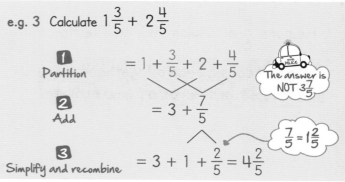

e.g. 3   Calculate $1\frac{3}{5} + 2\frac{4}{5}$

1 Partition $= 1 + \frac{3}{5} + 2 + \frac{4}{5}$

2 Add $= 3 + \frac{7}{5}$

The answer is NOT $3\frac{7}{5}$

$\frac{7}{5} = 1\frac{2}{5}$

3 Simplify and recombine $= 3 + 1 + \frac{2}{5} = 4\frac{2}{5}$

We can also add mixed numbers with different denominators ...

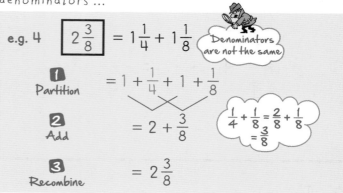

e.g. 4 $\boxed{2\frac{3}{8}} = 1\frac{1}{4} + 1\frac{1}{8}$

Denominators are not the same

1 Partition $= 1 + \frac{1}{4} + 1 + \frac{1}{8}$

2 Add $= 2 + \frac{3}{8}$

$\frac{1}{4} + \frac{1}{8} = \frac{2}{8} + \frac{1}{8}$
$= \frac{3}{8}$

3 Recombine $= 2\frac{3}{8}$

SET?

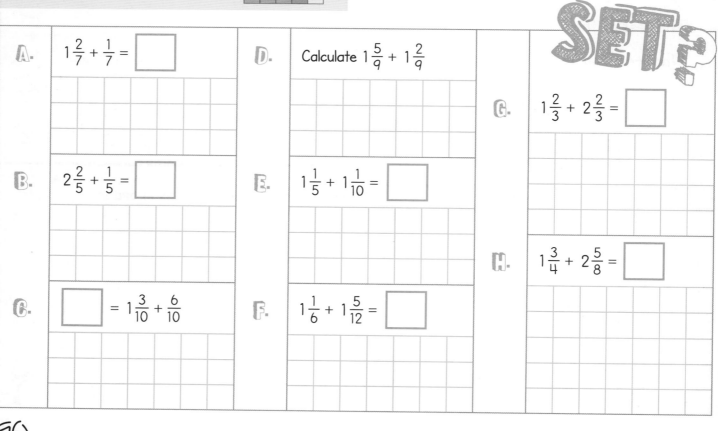

A. $1\frac{2}{7} + \frac{1}{7} = \boxed{}$

B. $2\frac{2}{5} + \frac{1}{5} = \boxed{}$

C. $\boxed{} = 1\frac{3}{10} + \frac{6}{10}$

D. Calculate $1\frac{5}{9} + 1\frac{2}{9}$

E. $1\frac{1}{5} + 1\frac{1}{10} = \boxed{}$

F. $1\frac{1}{6} + 1\frac{5}{12} = \boxed{}$

G. $1\frac{2}{3} + 2\frac{2}{3} = \boxed{}$

H. $1\frac{3}{4} + 2\frac{5}{8} = \boxed{}$

GO!

ADDING MIXED NUMBERS

1. Find the missing digits.

$$1\frac{\square}{7} + \square\frac{3}{7} = 3\frac{5}{\square}$$

2. Ahmed writes:

$$1\frac{1}{3} + 1\frac{1}{6} = 2\frac{2}{9}$$

Ahmed is not correct. Explain why.

3. The numbers in the sequence increase by the same amount each time.

Find the missing numbers.

$$\square \ , \ 1\frac{1}{2} \ , \ 1\frac{3}{4} \ , \ \square \ , \ \square$$

4. The diagram shows a field:

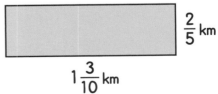

$\frac{2}{5}$ km

$1\frac{3}{10}$ km

Find the perimeter of the field.

km

We can subtract fractions with the same denominator by using our knowledge of subtraction:

five <u>dogs</u> subtract two <u>dogs</u> equals **three** <u>dogs</u>

$$50 - 20 = 30$$

five <u>tens</u> subtract two <u>tens</u> equals **three** <u>tens</u>

$$\frac{5}{6} - \frac{2}{6} = \frac{3}{6}$$

five <u>sixths</u> subtract two <u>sixths</u> equals **three** <u>sixths</u>

e.g. 1 $\quad \dfrac{5}{7} - \dfrac{1}{7} = \boxed{}$

Drawing a bar can be useful ...

$$\frac{5}{7} - \frac{1}{7} = \boxed{\frac{4}{7}}$$

$\frac{5}{7} - \frac{1}{7}$ does NOT equal $\frac{4}{0}$

We are left with four sevenths

When subtracting fractions with the same denominator, subtract the numerators ... but not the denominators

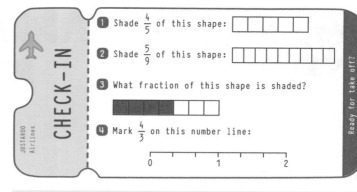

CHECK-IN

JUSTAROO Airlines

1 Shade $\frac{4}{5}$ of this shape:

2 Shade $\frac{5}{9}$ of this shape:

3 What fraction of this shape is shaded?

4 Mark $\frac{4}{3}$ on this number line:

0   1   2

Ready for take off?

e.g. 2 $\quad \dfrac{5}{8} - \dfrac{2}{8} = \boxed{\dfrac{3}{8}}$

We are left with three eighths

We can also think about subtracting fractions by counting backwards on a number line.

e.g. 3 Calculate $\dfrac{9}{7} - \dfrac{3}{7}$

1 Mark $\frac{9}{7}$ on a number line

2 Subtract $\frac{3}{7}$

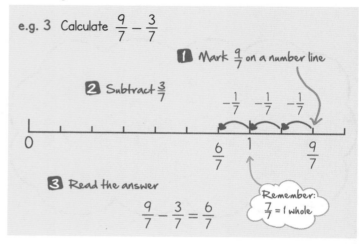

$-\frac{1}{7} \quad -\frac{1}{7} \quad -\frac{1}{7}$

0 $\qquad \frac{6}{7} \quad 1 \qquad \frac{9}{7}$

3 Read the answer

$$\frac{9}{7} - \frac{3}{7} = \frac{6}{7}$$

Remember: $\frac{7}{7} = 1$ whole

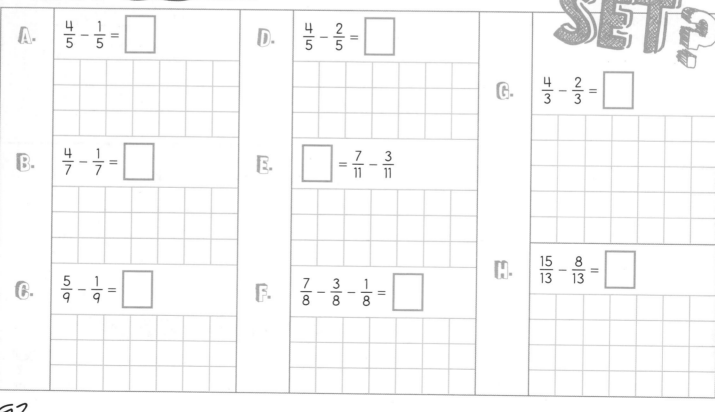

A. $\quad \dfrac{4}{5} - \dfrac{1}{5} = \boxed{}$

B. $\quad \dfrac{4}{7} - \dfrac{1}{7} = \boxed{}$

C. $\quad \dfrac{5}{9} - \dfrac{1}{9} = \boxed{}$

D. $\quad \dfrac{4}{5} - \dfrac{2}{5} = \boxed{}$

E. $\quad \boxed{} = \dfrac{7}{11} - \dfrac{3}{11}$

F. $\quad \dfrac{7}{8} - \dfrac{3}{8} - \dfrac{1}{8} = \boxed{}$

G. $\quad \dfrac{4}{3} - \dfrac{2}{3} = \boxed{}$

H. $\quad \dfrac{15}{13} - \dfrac{8}{13} = \boxed{}$

1. The length of some ribbon is 1 metre.

Chen and Jo each cut off a piece of ribbon.

Chen cuts off a piece $\frac{1}{10}$ of the length.

Jo cuts off a piece $\frac{3}{10}$ of the length.

What fraction of the ribbon is left?

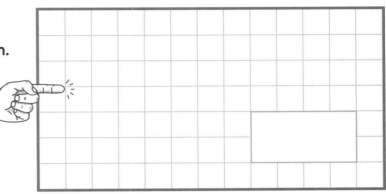

2. Find the missing digits.

$$\frac{13}{1\,\square} - \frac{\square}{\square\,2} = \frac{4}{1\,\square}$$

3. Freda writes:

$$1 - \frac{1}{5} = \frac{0}{5}$$

Explain why Freda is not correct.

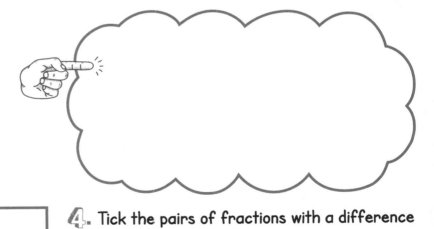

4. Tick the pairs of fractions with a difference less than one quarter.

$\frac{5}{8}$ and $\frac{2}{8}$ $\square$

$\frac{9}{16}$ and $\frac{5}{16}$ $\square$

$\frac{8}{5}$ and $\frac{7}{5}$ $\square$

$\frac{7}{6}$ and $\frac{5}{6}$ $\square$

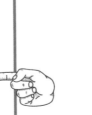

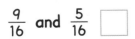

As with adding fractions, we can subtract fractions with different denominators by using equivalent fractions with **common denominators**.

$\frac{1}{5} - \frac{1}{15}$ is equivalent to $\frac{3}{15} - \frac{1}{15}$ ← common denominator

Denominators are not the same

because:  $\frac{1}{5} = \frac{3}{15}$

e.g. 1 $\frac{1}{3} - \frac{1}{6} = \Box$

We could start by drawing a bar showing $\frac{1}{3}$ ...

... but how do we take away $\frac{1}{6}$?

Drawing a bar using equivalent fractions is better

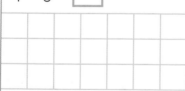 $\frac{1}{3} - \frac{1}{6} = \frac{2}{6} - \frac{1}{6} = \frac{1}{6}$

Denominators are now the same

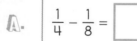 $\frac{1}{3} - \frac{1}{6} = \boxed{\frac{1}{6}}$

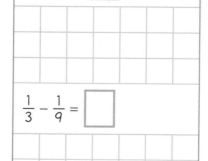
When subtracting fractions with different denominators, first find a common denominator

 CHECK-IN JUSTAROO Airlines Ready for take off?

1. $\frac{3}{8} - \frac{1}{8} =$

2. Circle all the fractions equivalent to $\frac{1}{2}$:
   $\frac{2}{4}$ $\frac{1}{5}$ $\frac{3}{6}$ $\frac{4}{8}$

3. Circle all the fractions equivalent to $\frac{3}{4}$:
   $\frac{4}{5}$ $\frac{6}{8}$ $\frac{9}{12}$ $\frac{2}{3}$

e.g. 2 $\frac{1}{2} - \frac{3}{10} = \boxed{\frac{2}{10}}$

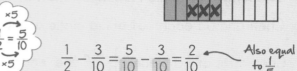

 $\frac{1}{2} = \frac{5}{10}$ (×5)

$\frac{1}{2} - \frac{3}{10} = \frac{5}{10} - \frac{3}{10} = \frac{2}{10}$ ← Also equal to $\frac{1}{5}$

Sometimes we need to find equivalent fractions for both fractions ...

e.g. 3 Calculate $\frac{5}{8} - \frac{1}{12}$

1 Look for the lowest common multiple of 8 and 12

Multiples of 8 → 8, 16, 24, 32, ...
Multiples of 12 → 12, 24, 36, 48, ...

2 Find equivalent fractions for $\frac{5}{8}$ and $\frac{1}{12}$

$\frac{5}{8} = \frac{15}{24}$ (×3) $\frac{1}{12} = \frac{2}{24}$ (×2)

3 Rewrite the calculation using fractions with the common denominator

$\frac{5}{8} - \frac{1}{12} = \frac{15}{24} - \frac{2}{24} = \frac{13}{24}$

SET

A. $\frac{1}{4} - \frac{1}{8} = \Box$

B. $\frac{1}{5} - \frac{1}{10} = \Box$

C. $\frac{1}{3} - \frac{1}{9} = \Box$

D. $\frac{7}{8} - \frac{1}{2} = \Box$

E. $\Box = \frac{7}{9} - \frac{1}{3}$

F. $\frac{11}{12} - \frac{2}{3} - \frac{1}{6} = \Box$

G. $\frac{3}{4} - \frac{1}{6} = \Box$

H. $\frac{3}{4} - \frac{2}{5} = \Box$

GO!

SUBTRACTING FRACTIONS 2

Canny good!

1. Josh and Ana are painting a wall.

   Josh paints $\frac{1}{5}$ of the wall.

   Altogether $\frac{11}{20}$ of the wall has been painted.

   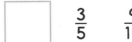 **What fraction of the wall does Ana paint?**

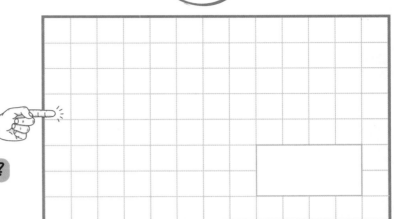

2. Here are some fractions:

   $$\frac{4}{12} \qquad \frac{2}{3} \qquad \frac{5}{6} \qquad \frac{8}{9}$$

   Find the two fractions that have a difference of $\frac{2}{9}$

3. Debbie thinks that:

   $$\frac{7}{12} - \frac{1}{4} = \frac{6}{8} = \frac{3}{4}$$

   Explain why Debbie is not correct.

4. The fractions in the sequence increase by the same amount each time.

   Find the missing fractions.

   $$\boxed{} \qquad \frac{3}{5} \qquad \frac{9}{10} \qquad \boxed{}$$

READY?

Sometimes we need to subtract either a proper fraction or a mixed number from another mixed number. We make connections with our knowledge of subtracting proper fractions to help.

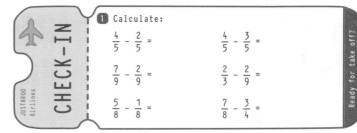
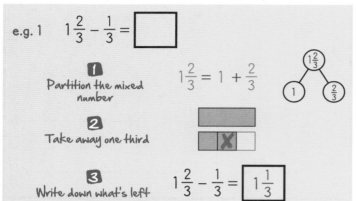

e.g. 1 $1\frac{2}{3} - \frac{1}{3} = \boxed{}$

1 Partition the mixed number $1\frac{2}{3} = 1 + \frac{2}{3}$

2 Take away one third

3 Write down what's left $1\frac{2}{3} - \frac{1}{3} = \boxed{1\frac{1}{3}}$

A number line is sometimes really helpful ...

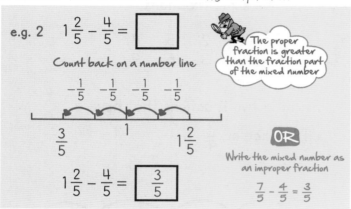

e.g. 2 $1\frac{2}{5} - \frac{4}{5} = \boxed{}$

Count back on a number line

The proper fraction is greater than the fraction part of the mixed number

$-\frac{1}{5}$ $-\frac{1}{5}$ $-\frac{1}{5}$ $-\frac{1}{5}$

$\frac{3}{5}$ 1 $1\frac{2}{5}$

$1\frac{2}{5} - \frac{4}{5} = \boxed{\frac{3}{5}}$

OR

Write the mixed number as an improper fraction

$\frac{7}{5} - \frac{4}{5} = \frac{3}{5}$

We can subtract mixed numbers with the same denominator ...

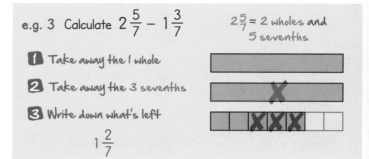

e.g. 3 Calculate $2\frac{5}{7} - 1\frac{3}{7}$ $2\frac{5}{7}$ = 2 wholes and 5 sevenths

1 Take away the 1 whole

2 Take away the 3 sevenths

3 Write down what's left

$1\frac{2}{7}$

Sometimes the denominators are different ...

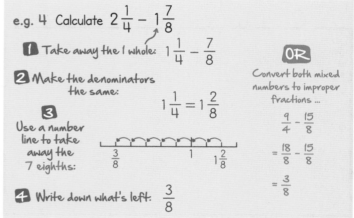

e.g. 4 Calculate $2\frac{1}{4} - 1\frac{7}{8}$

1 Take away the 1 whole: $1\frac{1}{4} - \frac{7}{8}$

2 Make the denominators the same: $1\frac{1}{4} = 1\frac{2}{8}$

3 Use a number line to take away the 7 eighths:

$\frac{3}{8}$ 1 $1\frac{2}{8}$

4 Write down what's left: $\frac{3}{8}$

OR

Convert both mixed numbers to improper fractions ...

$\frac{9}{4} - \frac{15}{8}$

$= \frac{18}{8} - \frac{15}{8}$

$= \frac{3}{8}$

SET?

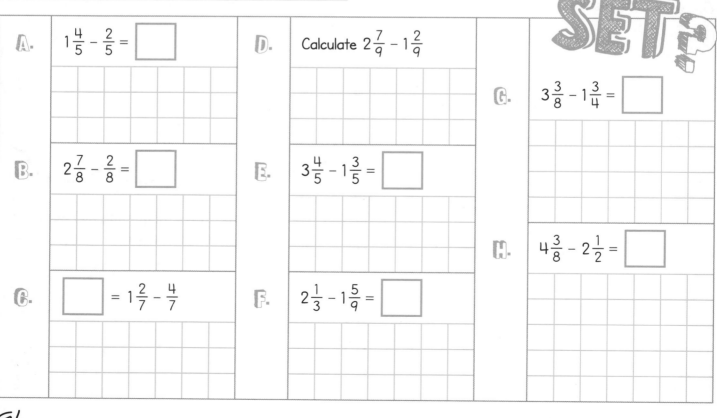

A. $1\frac{4}{5} - \frac{2}{5} = \boxed{}$

B. $2\frac{7}{8} - \frac{2}{8} = \boxed{}$

C. $\boxed{} = 1\frac{2}{7} - \frac{4}{7}$

D. Calculate $2\frac{7}{9} - 1\frac{2}{9}$

E. $3\frac{4}{5} - 1\frac{3}{5} = \boxed{}$

F. $2\frac{1}{3} - 1\frac{5}{9} = \boxed{}$

G. $3\frac{3}{8} - 1\frac{3}{4} = \boxed{}$

H. $4\frac{3}{8} - 2\frac{1}{2} = \boxed{}$

GO! SUBTRACTING MIXED NUMBERS

1. Find the missing numbers.

$$2\frac{\square}{7} - \square\frac{3}{7} = \frac{6}{\square}$$

2. Anika writes:

$$3\frac{1}{5} - 1\frac{4}{5} = 2\frac{3}{5}$$

Do you agree? Explain your thinking.

3. The difference between two mixed numbers is $\frac{1}{3}$

One of the numbers is $1\frac{8}{9}$

Find two possible values for the other number.

4. Dana buys a $3\frac{1}{2}$ litre can of paint.

She uses $1\frac{3}{4}$ litres to paint the walls.

How much paint does she have left?

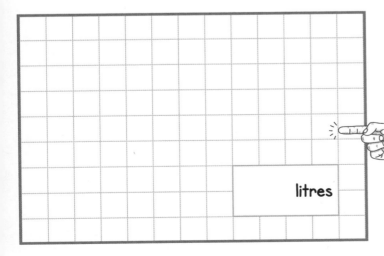

litres

We can multiply a fraction by a whole number using our knowledge of multiplying a whole number by a whole number. For example:

4×3 can be read as 'four' 3 times

$4 \times 3 = 12$

$\frac{1}{4} \times 3$ can be read as 'one quarter' 3 times

$\frac{1}{4} \times 3 = \frac{3}{4}$

 When multiplying a proper fraction by a whole number, only multiply the numerator and whole number together

e.g. 1 $\frac{1}{5} \times 3 = \boxed{}$

We can read this as $\frac{1}{5}$ three times

$\frac{1}{5} \times 3 = \boxed{\frac{3}{5}}$

The numerator is not always 1 ...

e.g. 2 Calculate $\frac{3}{7} \times 4$

Write your answer as a mixed number.

❶ Multiply the numerator by 4: $\frac{3}{7} \times 4 = \frac{12}{7}$

❷ Convert the improper fraction to a mixed number: $\frac{12}{7} = 1\frac{5}{7}$

JUSTAROO Airlines

CHECK-IN

1 True or false: $\frac{9}{4} = 2\frac{1}{9}$?

2 True or false: $2\frac{1}{3} = \frac{7}{3}$?

3 Circle the mixed number equivalent to $\frac{13}{5}$:

$1\frac{3}{5}$ $\quad 2\frac{3}{5}$ $\quad 3\frac{2}{5}$ $\quad 1\frac{8}{5}$

Ready for take off?

We can multiply mixed numbers by a whole number:

e.g. 3 $2\frac{1}{7} \times 3 = \boxed{}$

Altogether there are 6 wholes ...
... and three sevenths

Recombine to make a mixed number: $\quad 2\frac{1}{7} \times 3 = \boxed{6\frac{3}{7}}$

e.g. 4 Calculate $2\frac{4}{5} \times 3$

❶ Partition the mixed number into 2 and $\frac{4}{5}$

❷ Multiply the 2 by 3: $\quad 2 \times 3 = 6$

❸ Multiply the $\frac{4}{5}$ by 3: $\qquad$ ❹ Convert the improper fraction to a mixed number:

$\frac{4}{5} \times 3 = \frac{12}{5}$ $\qquad\qquad \frac{12}{5} = 2\frac{2}{5}$

❺ Recombine: $\quad 6 + 2\frac{2}{5} = 8\frac{2}{5}$

OR

The answer is NOT $6\frac{12}{5}$

Convert the mixed numbers to improper fractions ...

$2\frac{4}{5} \times 3 = \frac{14}{5} \times 3 = \frac{42}{5} = 8\frac{2}{5}$

... but this sometimes results in having to multiply large numbers

A. (i) $\frac{1}{5} \times 4 = \boxed{}$

(ii) $\frac{1}{7} \times 3 = \boxed{}$

(iii) $5 \times \frac{1}{8} = \boxed{}$

C. (i) $1\frac{2}{9} \times 4 = \boxed{}$

(ii) $\boxed{} = 3\frac{1}{5} \times 2$

(iii) $2\frac{3}{10} \times 3 = \boxed{}$

B. Calculate, giving each answer as a mixed number:

(i) $\frac{3}{5} \times 4$

(ii) $\frac{8}{9} \times 2$

(iii) $5 \times \frac{1}{4}$

D. Work out:

(i) $1\frac{4}{5} \times 4$

(ii) $2 \times 3\frac{5}{7}$

(iii) $4 \times 2\frac{3}{4}$

GO! MULTIPLYING A FRACTION

1. Complete the statement in two different ways:

$$\frac{\square}{\square} \times \square = \frac{6}{9}$$

$$\frac{\square}{\square} \times \square = \frac{6}{9}$$

$$\frac{\square}{\square} \times \square = \frac{6}{9}$$

2. Tommy writes:

$$\frac{3}{5} \times 3 = \frac{9}{15}$$

Do you agree? Explain why.

3. Place the calculations in order from smallest to largest product.

$1\frac{1}{3} \times 2$	Smallest product
$\frac{7}{9} \times 4$	
$1\frac{5}{6} \times 2$	
$\frac{2}{3} \times 5$	Largest product

4. Dave runs 20 miles.

Anne runs 30 kilometres.

Who runs the furthest?

Explain your answer.

HINT: 1 mile is approximately $1\frac{3}{5}$ kilometres

READY?

 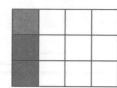

The green section is $\frac{1}{4}$ of the rectangle

The blue section is $\frac{1}{3}$ of $\frac{1}{4}$ of the rectangle

The blue section is also $\frac{1}{12}$ of the rectangle, so:

$$\frac{1}{3} \times \frac{1}{4} = \frac{1}{12}$$

We can multiply fractions by multiplying the numerators together, and multiplying the denominators together.

$$\frac{a}{b} \times \frac{c}{d} = \frac{a \times c}{b \times d}$$

e.g. 1 $\frac{1}{3} \times \frac{1}{2} = \square$

 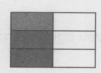

$\frac{1}{2}$ of the rectangle

$\frac{1}{3}$ of $\frac{1}{2} = \frac{1}{6}$

$$\frac{1}{3} \times \frac{1}{2} = \boxed{\frac{1}{6}}$$

JUSTAROO Airlines

CHECK-IN

Ready for take off?

1 Calculate:

$5 \times 5 =$ $3 \times 8 =$

$1 \times 2 \times 4 =$ $4 \times 5 \times 2 =$

2 Simplify $\frac{4}{10}$

3 True or false: $\frac{9}{15}$ cannot be simplified?

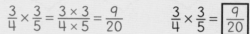

The numerator is not always 1 ...

e.g. 2 $\frac{2}{3} \times \frac{1}{5} = \square$

$$\frac{2}{3} \times \frac{1}{5} = \frac{2 \times 1}{3 \times 5} = \frac{2}{15}$$

1 Multiply the numerators

2 Multiply the denominators

$$\frac{2}{3} \times \frac{1}{5} = \boxed{\frac{2}{15}}$$

You do NOT need to find equivalent fractions when multiplying

e.g. 3 $\frac{3}{4} \times \frac{3}{5} = \square$

$$\frac{3}{4} \times \frac{3}{5} = \frac{3 \times 3}{4 \times 5} = \frac{9}{20} \qquad \frac{3}{4} \times \frac{3}{5} = \boxed{\frac{9}{20}}$$

Sometimes the final answer can be simplified ...

e.g. 4 Calculate $\frac{2}{5} \times \frac{1}{2}$. Simplify your answer.

$$\frac{2}{5} \times \frac{1}{2} = \frac{2 \times 1}{5 \times 2} = \frac{2}{10}$$

2 is a common factor of 2 and 10

$$\frac{2}{10} \overset{\div 2}{\underset{\div 2}{=}} \frac{1}{5}$$

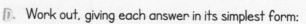

SET?

A. (i) $\frac{1}{5} \times \frac{1}{4} = \square$

  (ii) $\frac{1}{2} \times \frac{1}{6} = \square$

  (iii) $\square = \frac{1}{3} \times \frac{1}{3}$

B. (i) $\frac{2}{5} \times \frac{1}{3} = \square$

  (ii) $\square = \frac{1}{2} \times \frac{3}{4}$

  (iii) $\frac{2}{3} \times \frac{1}{3} = \square$

C. (i) $\square = \frac{2}{3} \times \frac{4}{5}$

  (ii) $\frac{2}{5} \times \frac{2}{5} = \square$

  (iii) $\frac{3}{4} \times \frac{3}{4} = \square$

D. Work out, giving each answer in its simplest form:

  (i) $\frac{1}{3} \times \frac{3}{4}$ (ii) $\frac{2}{5} \times \frac{1}{4}$

  (iii) $\frac{2}{3} \times \frac{5}{8}$ (iv) $\frac{1}{2} \times \frac{2}{3} \times \frac{3}{4}$

MULTIPLYING FRACTIONS

$$\frac{\square}{\square} \times \frac{\square}{\square} = \frac{1}{6}$$

1. Use the digits 1, 2, 3 and 4 to complete the statement.

2. Bailey is multiplying $\frac{1}{3}$ by $\frac{2}{5}$. She says,

"I need to use a common denominator of 15".

Do you agree with Bailey? Explain why.

3. Calculate $\left(\frac{2}{3}\right)^2$

HINT: $\left(\frac{2}{3}\right)^2$ means $\frac{2}{3}$ squared

4. Tick the calculations with a product greater than $\frac{1}{5}$

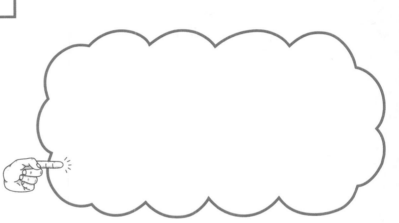

$\frac{1}{3} \times \frac{1}{3}$ $\frac{2}{3} \times \frac{1}{4}$ $\frac{1}{2} \times \frac{1}{2}$

$\frac{4}{5} \times \frac{1}{3}$ $\frac{1}{4} \times \frac{3}{5}$

5. A bottle contains $\frac{3}{4}$ of a litre of lemonade.

Gwyn drinks one third of the lemonade.

How much lemonade does Gwyn drink?

ml

READY?

We can think about dividing fractions by a whole number in different ways. For example:

Whole-part-part model

e.g. $\frac{3}{4} \div 3$ can be thought about the same way as sharing 3 counters equally between 3 people:

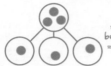

3 counters shared equally between 3 people = 1 counter each

$\frac{3}{4} \div 3 = \frac{1}{4}$

e.g. 1 $\frac{4}{5} \div 4 = \boxed{}$

The numerator is the same as the divisor ... $4 \div 4 = 1$

$\frac{4}{5} \div 4 = \boxed{\frac{1}{5}}$

If the numerator is not the same as the divisor ...

Bar model

e.g. $\frac{1}{4} \div 2$

$\div 2$

$\frac{1}{4} \div 2 = \frac{1}{8}$

We could also think about $\frac{1}{4} \div 2$ by using the fact that dividing by 2 is equivalent to multiplying by $\frac{1}{2}$

This is one half of one quarter

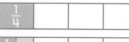

$\frac{1}{4} \div 2 = \frac{1}{4} \times \frac{1}{2}$

$= \frac{1}{8}$

JUSTAROO Airlines

CHECK-IN

Ready for take off?

1. $\frac{1}{3} = \frac{\boxed{}}{9}$ $\frac{3}{5} = \frac{\boxed{}}{10}$ $\frac{\boxed{}}{4} = \frac{6}{8}$

$\frac{5}{\boxed{}} = \frac{15}{18}$ $\frac{1}{4} = \frac{4}{\boxed{}}$ $\frac{\boxed{}}{5} = \frac{3}{\boxed{}}$

2. $\frac{\boxed{}}{\boxed{}} = \frac{\boxed{}}{\boxed{}} = \frac{8}{12}$

e.g. 2 $\frac{1}{3} \div 2 = \boxed{}$

$\div 2$

$\frac{1}{3}$

$\frac{1}{6}$

Think about this calculation as:

$\frac{1}{3} \div 2 = \frac{1}{3} \times \frac{1}{2} = \frac{1}{6}$

OR

$\frac{1}{3} \div 2 = \boxed{\frac{1}{6}}$

We can also use equivalent fractions when the calculation is more complex ...

e.g. 3 $\frac{2}{5} \div 3 = \boxed{}$

$\times 3$

$\frac{2}{5} = \frac{6}{15}$

$\times 3$

1 Write the numerator as a multiple of the divisor using equivalent fractions

2 Rewrite the calculation: $\frac{2}{5} \div 3 = \frac{6}{15} \div 3$

3 Solve:

$\frac{6}{15}$

$\frac{2}{15}$ $\frac{2}{15}$ $\frac{2}{15}$

Think about this calculation as:

$\frac{2}{5} \div 3 = \frac{2}{5} \times \frac{1}{3} = \frac{2}{15}$

OR

$\frac{2}{5} \div 3 = \boxed{\frac{2}{15}}$

SET?

A. (i) $\frac{3}{7} \div 3 = \boxed{}$

(ii) $\frac{3}{5} \div 3 = \boxed{}$

(iii) $\boxed{} = \frac{4}{9} \div 4$

B. (i) $\frac{1}{5} \div 2 = \boxed{}$

(ii) $\boxed{} = \frac{1}{2} \div 3$

(iii) $\frac{1}{4} \div 4 = \boxed{}$

C. (i) $\boxed{} = \frac{3}{5} \div 2$

(ii) $\frac{3}{4} \div 2 = \boxed{}$

(iii) $\frac{5}{6} \div 3 = \boxed{}$

D. Calculate:

(i) $\frac{1}{12} \div 3$

(ii) $\frac{5}{12} \div 4$

(iii) $\frac{2}{15} \div 5$

(iv) $\frac{3}{13} \div 10$

GO!

DIVIDING A FRACTION

1. Describe the green square using a multiplication statement and a division statement:

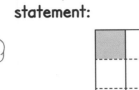

2. Stevie writes:

$$\frac{3}{12} \div 3 = \frac{1}{4}$$

Do you agree? Explain your answer.

3. Find the missing digits.

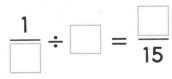

$$\frac{1}{\square} \div \square = \frac{\square}{15}$$

4. Match each calculation with the order of its answer starting with the smallest.

$\frac{4}{9} \div 2$	1st	Smallest answer
$\frac{1}{5} \div 2$	2nd	
$\frac{1}{3} \div 3$	3rd	
$\frac{6}{7} \div 3$	4th	Largest answer

5. A length of string is $\frac{3}{5}$ of a metre.

The string is cut into four equal lengths.

How long is each piece of string?

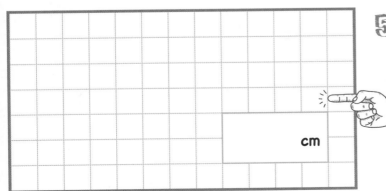

cm

READY?

Fractions with a denominator of 10 or 100 (and so on) can easily be written as decimals using place value:

$$\frac{3}{10} = 3 \text{ tenths} = 0.3 \quad \text{and} \quad \frac{3}{100} = 3 \text{ hundredths} = 0.03$$

Other fractions can also be expressed as a decimal using equivalent fractions. For example:

$$\frac{2}{5} \quad \text{is equivalent to} \quad \frac{4}{10}$$

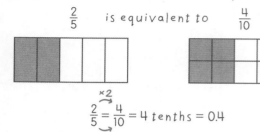

$$\frac{2}{5} \overset{\times 2}{\underset{\times 2}{=}} \frac{4}{10} = 4 \text{ tenths} = 0.4$$

e.g. 1 Write $\frac{3}{5}$ as a decimal.

$$\frac{3}{5} \overset{\times 2}{\underset{\times 2}{=}} \frac{6}{10}$$

Find an equivalent fraction with a denominator of 10

$$\frac{6}{10} = 0.6$$

0.6 is 6 tenths

Sometimes it's easier to find an equivalent fraction with a denominator of 100 ...

e.g. 2 Write $\frac{3}{20}$ as a decimal.

$$\frac{3}{20} \overset{\times 5}{\underset{\times 5}{=}} \frac{15}{100} = 0.15$$

Find an equivalent fraction with a denominator of 100

Ready for take off?

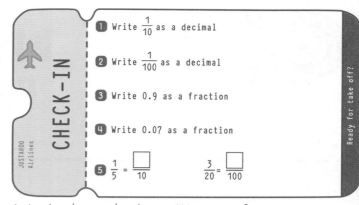

CHECK-IN

JUSTAROO Airlines

1. Write $\frac{1}{10}$ as a decimal

2. Write $\frac{1}{100}$ as a decimal

3. Write 0.9 as a fraction

4. Write 0.07 as a fraction

5. $\frac{1}{5} = \frac{\square}{10}$ $\qquad$ $\frac{3}{20} = \frac{\square}{100}$

A decimal can also be written as a fraction ...

e.g. 3 Write 0.18 as a fraction in its simplest form.

$$0.18 = \frac{18}{100}$$ 0.18 is 18 hundredths

$$\frac{18}{100} \overset{\div 2}{\underset{\div 2}{=}} \frac{9}{50}$$

Simplify by finding a common factor

Some fractions are simplified by using factors other than 2 ...

e.g. 4 Write 0.35 as a fraction in its simplest form.

$$0.35 = \frac{35}{100}$$ 0.35 is 35 hundredths

$$\frac{35}{100} \overset{\div 5}{\underset{\div 5}{=}} \frac{7}{20}$$

Divide both the numerator and denominator by 5

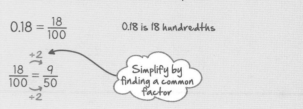

Fractions with denominators of 10, 100, 1,000 and so on can be written as decimals using place value

SET?

A. Write $\frac{4}{5}$ as a decimal.

B. Write $\frac{11}{20}$ as a decimal.

C. Write 0.17 as a fraction.

D. Write $\frac{11}{25}$ as a decimal.

E. Write 0.05 as a fraction in its simplest form.

F. Write 0.16 as a fraction in its simplest form.

GO!

FRACTIONS AND DECIMALS

1. Place the fractions and decimals in order from smallest to largest:

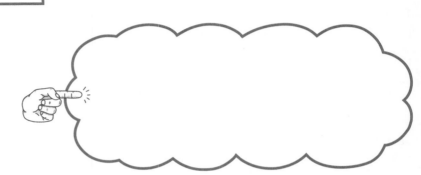

$$\frac{51}{100} \qquad \frac{1}{5} \qquad 1.5 \qquad \frac{1}{50} \qquad 0.15$$

2. Stuart thinks that:

$$\frac{9}{20} = 9.20$$

Explain why Stuart is not correct.

3. Use the digits 0, 1, 2, 3 and 5 to complete the statement.

$$\frac{\square}{\square\square} = 0.\square\square$$

4. Shade 0.45 of the rectangle.

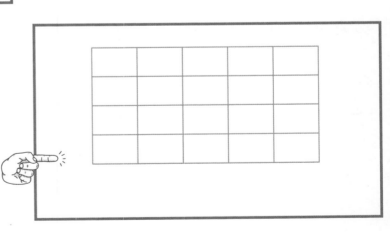

5. Alec runs 0.625 of a kilometre.

Val runs $\frac{13}{20}$ of a kilometre.

Who runs the furthest?

Give a reason for your answer.

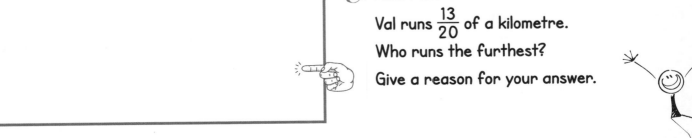

READY?

Percentages are fractions expressed 'out of one hundred'. Therefore they can easily be written as fractions and, using place value, as decimals.

$$1\% = \frac{1}{100} = 0.01$$
(one hundredth)

$$10\% = \frac{10}{100} = \frac{1}{10} = 0.10 = 0.1$$
(one tenth)

These facts can be used to convert other percentages to fractions and decimals, e.g. $5 \times 1\% = 5\% = \frac{5}{100} = 0.05$

It is also really useful to remember that:

$$50\% = \frac{1}{2} = 0.5$$ $$25\% = \frac{1}{4} = 0.25$$

e.g. 1a Write 7% as a fraction and as a decimal.

$$7\% = \frac{7}{100} = 0.07$$ 7% means '7 out of 100' or 7 hundredths

e.g. 1b Write 70% as a fraction and as a decimal.

$$70\% = \frac{70}{100} = \frac{7}{10}$$ 70% means '70 out of 100' or 70 hundredths

$$70\% = 0.70 = 0.7$$ We can write $\frac{70}{100}$ as $\frac{7}{10}$ and 0.70 as 0.7

Decimals can easily be written as a fraction and as a percentage ...

e.g. 2 Write 0.17 as a fraction and as a percentage.

$$0.17 = \frac{17}{100} = 17\%$$ 0.17 is 17 hundredths

Sometimes equivalent fractions are needed ...

e.g. 3 Write $\frac{3}{10}$ as a decimal and as a percentage.

$$\frac{3}{10} = 0.3$$ 0.3 is 3 tenths

$$\frac{3}{10} = \frac{30}{100} = 30\%$$ (×10)   Use equivalent fractions to write $\frac{3}{10}$ as a fraction with a denominator of 100

It's also useful to know and use the 'common' percentages (25% and 50%) ...

e.g. 4 Write 75% as a decimal and as a fraction.

$$75\% = 0.75$$ 75% means '75 out of 100' or 75 hundredths

$$75\% = \frac{3}{4}$$ 75% = 3 × 25% and we know that 25% = $\frac{1}{4}$ so 75% = 3 × $\frac{1}{4}$ = $\frac{3}{4}$

SET?

A. Write 3% as a fraction and as a decimal.

B. Write 90% as a fraction and as a decimal.

C. Write 0.23 as a fraction and as a percentage.

%

D. Write 0.33 as a fraction and as a percentage.

%

E. Write $\frac{6}{10}$ as a decimal and as a percentage.

%

FRACTIONS, DECIMALS AND PERCENTAGES

Amazing!

1. Place the fractions, decimals and percentages in order from smallest to largest:

4% 4.5 0.4 $\dfrac{5}{10}$ $\dfrac{45}{100}$

2. Yolanda thinks that:

$$3\% = 0.3$$

Explain why Yolanda is not correct.

3. Use the digits 1, 2, 4 and 5 to complete the statement.

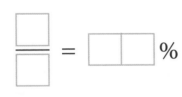

4. Taylor gets 68% in a test.

Kitty scores 17 out of 20 in the same test.

Who gets the highest test score?

Explain your answer.

5. Andrea, Briony and Cam share the price of a pizza.

Andrea pays for 55% of the pizza.

Briony pays for one quarter of the pizza.

Cam pays £2

How much do they pay altogether for the pizza?

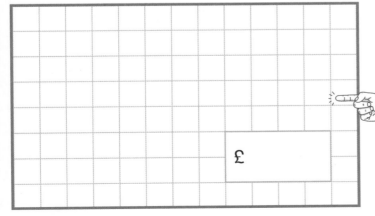

READY?

As percentages can be written as fractions, the method to find a percentage of an amount is similar to finding a fraction of an amount.

Some percentage-fraction equivalents are very useful to know:

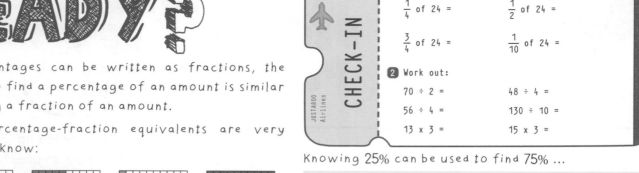

1 Find:

$\frac{1}{4}$ of 24 = $\frac{1}{2}$ of 24 =

$\frac{3}{4}$ of 24 = $\frac{1}{10}$ of 24 =

2 Work out:

70 ÷ 2 =   48 ÷ 4 =

56 ÷ 4 =   130 ÷ 10 =

13 x 3 =   15 x 3 =

To find 50% of an amount is the same as finding $\frac{1}{2}$

To find 25% of an amount is the same as finding $\frac{1}{4}$

To find 10% of an amount is the same as finding $\frac{1}{10}$

To find 75% of an amount is the same as finding $\frac{3}{4}$

Knowing 25% can be used to find 75% ...

e.g. 1   Find 50% of 16

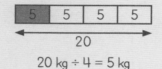

| 8 | 8 |

16

To find 50% of an amount is the same as finding $\frac{1}{2}$

The whole is 16

16 ÷ 2 = 8

e.g. 2b   Find 75% of 20 kg

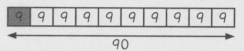

| 5 | 5 | 5 | 5 |

20

To find 75% of an amount is the same as finding $\frac{3}{4}$ ...

... also the same as multiplying 25% by 3

I know that 25% of 20 kg is 5 kg

so 75% of 20 kg = 5 kg × 3 = 15 kg

e.g. 2a   Find 25% of 20 kg

| 5 | 5 | 5 | 5 |

20

To find 25% of an amount is the same as finding $\frac{1}{4}$

20 kg ÷ 4 = 5 kg

e.g. 3   Find 10% of £90

| 9 | 9 | 9 | 9 | 9 | 9 | 9 | 9 | 9 | 9 |

90

To find 10% of an amount is the same as finding $\frac{1}{10}$

£90 ÷ 10 = £9

Do NOT forget units!

$10\% = \frac{1}{10}$ $25\% = \frac{1}{4}$ $50\% = \frac{1}{2}$ $75\% = \frac{3}{4}$

SET?

A. Find 50% of 24	**D.** Find 10% of £70
B. Find 25% of 48	**E.** Work out 10% of £65
C. Calculate 75% of 80	**F.** Calculate 75% of 120 kg

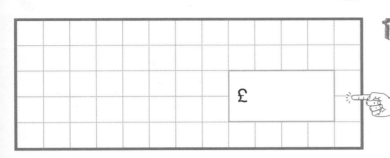

PERCENTAGE OF AN AMOUNT 1

Wicked!

1. A sale has 25% off all prices.
A television normally costs £240.
Find the sale price of the television.

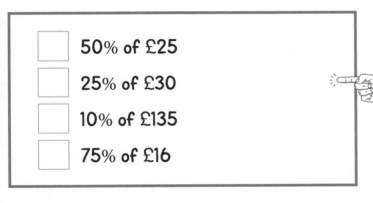
£

2. Insert <, > or = to make the statement correct.

25% of 10 ◯ 10% of 25

3. Tick the calculation with the greatest value.

☐ 50% of £25
☐ 25% of £30
☐ 10% of £135
☐ 75% of £16

4. George gets 75% in a test.
Lucy scores 57 out of 80 in the same test.
Who gets the greatest number of marks?
Explain your answer.

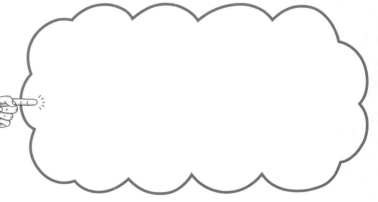

5. Use the digits 3, 4, 5, 6, 7 and 8 to complete the statement.

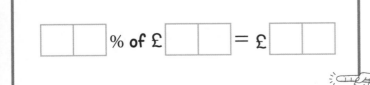
[ ][ ] % of £[ ][ ] = £[ ][ ]

READY?

10% of an amount can be found by dividing by 10. This fact can be used to find other percentages. For example:

* 30% of an amount = 3 times 10% of the amount
* 5% of an amount = $\frac{1}{2}$ of 10% of the amount

Harder percentages, such as 35%, can be found by combining other percentages. For example:

* 35% of an amount = 30% of the amount + 5% of the amount

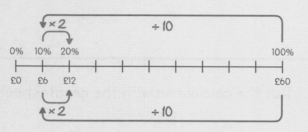
If I know 10% then I also know ...

e.g. 1   Find 20% of £60

1 10% of £60 = £6
2 20% of £60 = £6 × 2 = £12

20% of 60 is NOT 60 ÷ 20

1 Write as a fraction in its simplest form:

30% =   50% =

70% =   90% =

2 Find:

25% of 12 =   50% of 60 =

75% of 20 =   10% of 45 =

Sometimes the solution is not a whole number ...

e.g. 2   Find 5% of £70

Find 10% first → 10% of £70 = £7
5% of £70 = £3.50   ⟩ ÷2

We can use percentages in different ways ...

e.g. 3   Find 35% of 200 kg

5% of 200 kg = 10 kg   ⟩ ÷2
Find 10% first → 10% of 200 kg = 20 kg
30% of 200 kg = 60 kg   ⟩ ×3

35% of 200 kg = 30% of 200 kg + 5% of 200 kg
= 60 kg + 10 kg
= 70 kg

e.g. 4   Find 95% of 400 m

Find 10% first → 10% of 400 m = 40 m
5% of 400 m = 20 m   ⟩ ÷2

95% of 400 m = 100% of 400 m − 5% of 400 m
= 400 m − 20 m
= 380 m

SET?

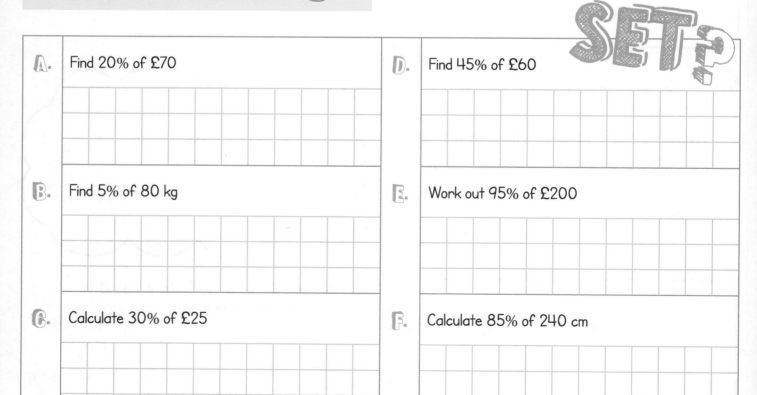

A. Find 20% of £70

B. Find 5% of 80 kg

C. Calculate 30% of £25

D. Find 45% of £60

E. Work out 95% of £200

F. Calculate 85% of 240 cm

GO!

PERCENTAGE OF AN AMOUNT 2

1. Write a digit in each box to complete the statement.

☐☐ % of 20 = 13

2. Hayley thinks that to find 20% of £80 she needs to divide £80 by 20

Do you agree? Explain your answer.

3. Trevor is making 1 litre of fruit smoothie.

$\frac{1}{4}$ of the smoothie is apple.

45% of the smoothie is banana.

The rest of the smoothie is mango.

How many millilitres of the smoothie is mango?

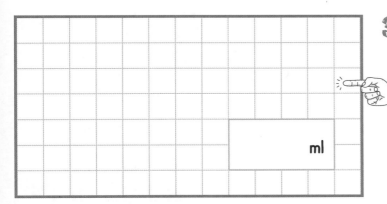

ml

4. Grandma Marg wins £250

She gives 60% to one grandchild.

She gives £60 to her other grandchild.

How much money does Grandma Marg have left?

5. Which of the following statements is true?

    A. 15% of 30 > 30% of 15

    B. 15% of 30 = 30% of 15

    C. 15% of 30 < 30% of 15

Explain your answer.

Trickier percentages such as 3%, 36% and 99% can still be found by finding 10% first. We can then use this fact to find other percentages such as 5% and 1%, and combine as needed.

For example: 26% = 20% + 5% + 1%

Remember, for any amount:

* 20% is two times 10% of the amount

* 5% is half of 10% of the amount

* 1% can be found by dividing the amount by 10 and then by 10 again (or dividing by 100)

e.g. 1   Find 36% of £300

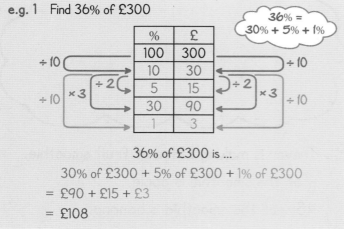

36% = 30% + 5% + 1%

%	£
100	300
10	30
5	15
30	90
1	3

36% of £300 is ...

30% of £300 + 5% of £300 + 1% of £300

= £90 + £15 + £3

= £108

Divide by 10 for 10% ... divide by 10 again for 1%

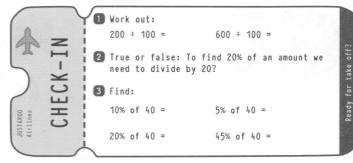

CHECK-IN

JUSTAROO Airlines

1. Work out:

200 ÷ 100 =   600 ÷ 100 =

2. True or false: To find 20% of an amount we need to divide by 20?

3. Find:

10% of 40 =   5% of 40 =

20% of 40 =   45% of 40 =

Ready for take off?

Sometimes it is sensible to find 1% first ...

e.g. 2   Find 3% of 500

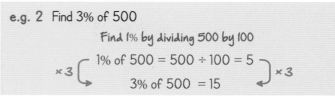

Find 1% by dividing 500 by 100

×3 { 1% of 500 = 500 ÷ 100 = 5 } ×3
    3% of 500 = 15

More complex percentages of an amount can be found using different strategies ...

e.g. 3   Find 99% of 250 kg

%	kg
100	250
1	2.5

÷100   ÷100

99% of 250 kg = 100% of 250 kg − 1% of 250 kg

= 250 kg − 2.5 kg

= 247.5 kg

OR

99% = 10% of 250 kg × 9 + 1% of 250 kg × 9

= 225 kg + 22.5 kg

= 247.5 kg

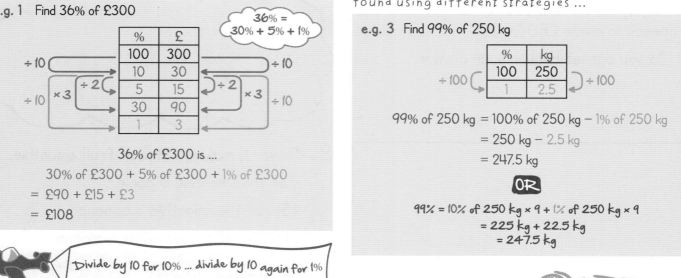

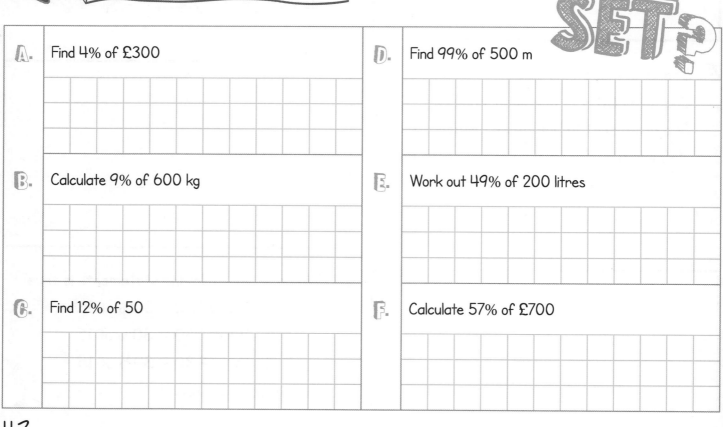

A. Find 4% of £300

B. Calculate 9% of 600 kg

C. Find 12% of 50

D. Find 99% of 500 m

E. Work out 49% of 200 litres

F. Calculate 57% of £700

 **PERCENTAGE OF AN AMOUNT 3**

Fantastic!

1. Place the digits 0, 1 and 2 to complete the statement.

☐ 1% of 2 ☐ 0 = ☐ 2

2. Find the missing number.

☐ % of 50 = 43

3. Gabriel thinks that to find 9% of £60 he needs to divide £60 by 9

Do you agree? Explain your answer.

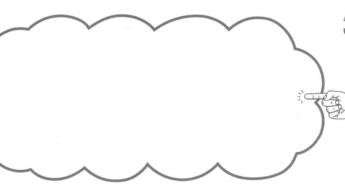

4. A train ticket costs £75

The price of the ticket increases by 14%.

What is the new price of the train ticket?

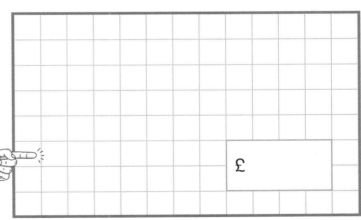

£

5. Insert <, > or = to make the statement correct.

51% of 200 ◯ 24% of 400

READY?

We can read and write times on (analogue) clock faces using words such as:

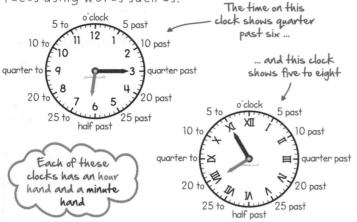

The time on this clock shows quarter past six ...

... and this clock shows five to eight

Each of these clocks has an hour hand and a minute hand

Times before 12 noon (midday) are written using a.m. and times after 12 noon are written using p.m.

Times can also be displayed using digital clocks. For example, twenty past ten in the morning is

10:20

e.g. 1 Draw hands on the clock to show the time 3:10 a.m.

The minute hand points at '10 past'

The hour hand points a little way past the 3

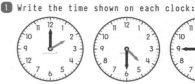

Using numbers and words ...

e.g. 2 The clock shows a time in the afternoon.
Write the time shown on the clock:
(i) using words   (ii) using a.m./p.m.

1 The hour hand is between 2 and 3 so it is 'something to 3'

2 The minute hand is pointing at '20 to'

(i) Twenty to three   (ii) 2:40 p.m.

We can also write times using 24-hour clock notation:

e.g. 3 Write the time shown on this clock using 24-hour clock notation if it is:
(i) morning   (ii) afternoon

A number line can help ...

12-hour notation
12 midnight 1 a.m. 2 a.m. 3 a.m.   12 midday 1 p.m. 2 p.m. 3 p.m.
00:00 01:00 02:00 03:00   12:00 13:00 14:00 15:00
24-hour notation

24-hour clock times are always 4 digits

(i) 03:00   (ii) 15:00

We can convert between 12 and 24-hour clock times:

e.g. 4 Write these times in 12-hour clock notation:
(i) 11:20   (ii) 17:45

11:20 a.m. → 5:45 p.m.
11:20   17:45   −12

(i) 11:20 a.m.
(ii) 5:45 p.m.

A. Draw hands on the clock to show:

(i) Ten to three   (ii) Twenty past one

B. Write the time shown on the clock using:
(i) a.m./p.m.
(ii) words

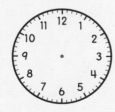

Evening

C. Write the time shown on the clock using:
(i) a.m./p.m.
(ii) words

Morning

D. Write the times using 24-hour clock notation:
(i) 5:20 a.m.
(ii) 9:30 p.m.
(iii) 11:45 a.m.
(iv) 10:50 p.m.

SET?

E. Write the times using 12-hour clock notation:
(i) 14:20
(ii) 07:50
(iii) 10:45
(iv) 00:05

GO!

TIME 1

1. Here is a time shown on a digital clock:

18:47

Draw hands on the analgue clock to show the same time.

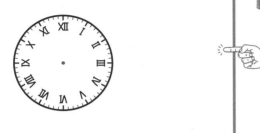

2. Monty thinks that this digital clock shows 6 p.m.

16:00

Explain why Monty is not correct.

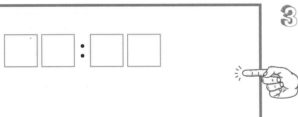

3. The angle between the minute hand and the hour hand on a clock is an acute angle.

Use the digits 1, 2, 3 and 4 to find a possible time written in 24-hour clock notation.

4. Look at the times listed.

a) Match each time with its description using 24-hour notation.

b) Find the missing description.

20 to 8 in the evening	17:40
20 to 6 in the evening	20:40
20 past 6 in the evening	19:40
20 past 8 in the evening	18:20
	20:20

5. A clock face is reflected in a mirror.

Write the two possible times in 24-hour clock notation.

The length of time taken for an event to happen is called the duration.

For example, if a film starts at 5:40 p.m. and finishes at 7 p.m. the duration of the film is 1 hour and 20 minutes.

A number line is very useful to help calculate the difference between start and finish times.

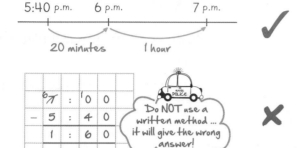

✓

Do NOT use a written method ... it will give the wrong answer!

✗

e.g. 1 A film starts at 7:25 p.m. and finishes at 9:05 p.m. What is the duration of the film?

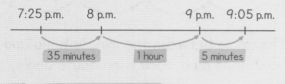

7:25 p.m. 8 p.m. 9 p.m. 9:05 p.m.

35 minutes | 1 hour | 5 minutes

1 hour + 35 minutes + 5 minutes = 1 hour and 40 minutes

CHECK-IN

JUSTAROO Airlines

1. Write the times using 24-hour clock notation:
   6:40 a.m.   7:30 p.m.
2. Write the times using 12-hour clock notation:
   16:35   06:20
3. True or false: 100 minutes = 1 hour?
4. A TV programme is 50 mins long. It starts at 5:05 p.m. What time does it finish?

Ready for take off?

We can find start (or end) times given the duration ...

e.g. 2 A TV programme is 2 hours and 12 minutes long.
It starts at 14:53
What time does the programme finish?

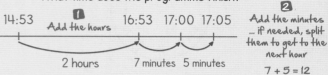

14:53   Add the hours   16:53   17:00 17:05

2 hours   7 minutes 5 minutes

Add the minutes ... if needed, split them to get to the next hour   7 + 5 = 12

The programme finishes at 17:05

We can also solve problems involving timetables ...

e.g. 3 Here is part of a train timetable from Cheltenham to Birmingham:

Cheltenham	10:04	10:13	10:32	10:55
Ashchurch	10:16	10:25	-	11:07
Bromsgrove	10:33	10:42	11:01	-
Birmingham	11:02	11:11	11:30	11:53

Does not stop here

(i) How many train journeys does the timetable show?
   4 train journeys   (Each column is one journey)

(ii) The duration of the journey is the same for all trains. How long is the journey from Cheltenham to Birmingham?
   Start time 10:04, Finish time 11:02   (Pick any train)
   10:04 → 11:00   11:00 → 11:02
   Duration = 56 minutes + 2 minutes = 58 minutes

A. Complete the table:

Start time	Finish time	Duration
3:15 p.m.	4:30 p.m.	
4:45 p.m.	5:10 p.m.	
5:50 p.m.	6:25 p.m.	
6:05 p.m.	7:55 p.m.	

B. Complete the table:

Start time	Finish time	Duration
07:23	08:15	
10:35		40 minutes
13:47		1 hour 25 minutes
	15:07	53 minutes

C. Here is a bus timetable:

Swinton	14:12	14:28	14:52	15:12
Monton	14:25	14:41	15:05	15:25
Eccles	14:45	15:01	-	15:45
Manchester	15:12	15:28	15:52	16:12

(i) The duration of the journey is the same for all buses. How long is the bus journey from Swinton to Manchester?

(ii) How many buses stop at Eccles?

(iii) Brenda wants to arrive in Manchester by 15:45. What is the latest bus she can catch from Swinton?

GO!

Hoot!

1. The duration of a train journey from Reading to Cardiff is 85 minutes.

   A train arrives in Cardiff at 7:15 p.m.

   What time did it leave Reading?

2. A television programme starts at 5:50 p.m. and finishes at 6:25 p.m.

   Hamish works out the duration of the programme:

   6.25 − 5.50 = 0.75 = 75 minutes

   Do you agree? Explain your answer.

3. Use the digits 1, 2, 3, 4 and 5 to complete the statement.

   The time between 0☐:☐0 and 0☐:1☐ is ☐5 minutes

4. Look at the train timetable:

Durham	16:40	16:52	17:20	17:45
Darlington	16:59	17:11	17:39	18:04
Northallerton	17:11	-	17:51	-
York	17.33	17:45	18:13	18:38

   a) How long does it take the 17:11 train from Darlington to reach York?

   b) Chad is meeting a friend at 6:30 p.m. in York. What is the latest train he can catch from Durham?

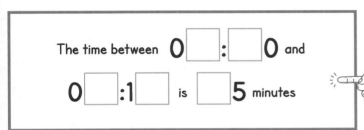

5. Match a start time to an end time and duration.

   One has been done for you.

18:10	6:50 p.m.	40 minutes
18:20	7:30 p.m.	50 minutes
18:30	7:40 p.m.	70 minutes
18:40	7:50 p.m.	80 minutes
18:50	8:10 p.m.	90 minutes

READY?

Length can be measured using different units. Small lengths are measured in millimetres (mm) and centimetres (cm). Longer lengths and distances are measured in metres (m) and kilometres (km).

We can convert between these units:

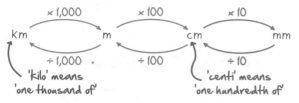

'kilo' means 'one thousand of'

'centi' means 'one hundredth of'

We can convert into smaller units ...

e.g. 1 Write 3 cm in millimetres.

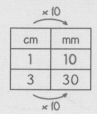

A table can be helpful to convert units

× 10

cm	mm
1	10
3	30

× 10

1 Recall ... 1 cm = 10 mm

2 Multiply by 10 to convert cm to mm

mm are smaller than cm ... expect an answer greater than 3

3 cm = 30 mm

e.g. 2 Convert 4.5 km to metres.

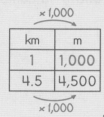

× 1,000

km	m
1	1,000
4.5	4,500

× 1,000

1 Recall ... 1 km = 1,000 m

2 Multiply by 1,000 to convert km to m

m are smaller than km ... expect an answer greater than 4.5

4.5 km = 4,500 m

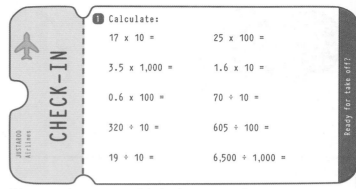
CHECK-IN

JUSTAROO Airlines

1 Calculate:

17 x 10 =   25 x 100 =

3.5 x 1,000 =   1.6 x 10 =

0.6 x 100 =   70 ÷ 10 =

320 ÷ 10 =   605 ÷ 100 =

19 ÷ 10 =   6,500 ÷ 1,000 =

Ready for take off?

We can also convert into larger units ...

e.g. 3 Write 405 cm in metres.

÷ 100

cm	m
100	1
405	4.05

÷ 100

1 Recall ... 100 cm = 1 m

2 Divide by 100 to convert cm to m

m are larger than cm ... expect an answer less than 405

405 cm = 4.05 m

e.g. 4 Convert 4,025 m to kilometres.

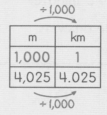

÷ 1,000

m	km
1,000	1
4,025	4.025

÷ 1,000

1 1,000 m = 1 km

2 Divide by 1,000 to convert m to km

km are larger than m ... expect an answer smaller than 4,025

4,025 m = 4.025 km

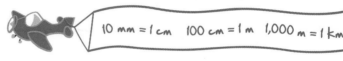

10 mm = 1 cm   100 cm = 1 m   1,000 m = 1 km

SET?

A. Complete the table:

cm	mm
7	
4	
1.8	
3.52	
0.9	

C. Complete the table:

cm	m
100	
	2
350	
	1.25
75	

B. Complete the table:

cm	mm
	10
	60
	25
	36
	8

D. Complete the table:

m	km
1,000	
	3
2,500	
	3.2
645	

E. Convert:

(i)   1.050 km to metres

(ii) 3.02 metres to centimetres

(iii) 0.4 centimetres to mm

(iv) 95 cm to m

Yay!

1. Tim has a 2.7 m length of wood.

He cuts it into 3 pieces.

The length of the first piece is 65 cm

The length of the second piece is 1.2 m

How long is the third piece of wood?

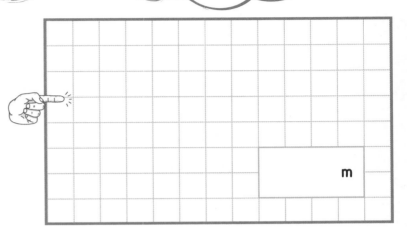

m

2. Sidney thinks:

$$1.2 \text{ cm} = 120 \text{ mm}$$

Do you agree? Explain your answer.

3. Max is running around a 400 metre running track.

How many laps does he complete to run 10 kilometres?

4. Kelly walks 6.25 km each week.

Rachel walks $5\frac{1}{2}$ km each week.

How many more metres does Kelly walk than Rachel each week?

m

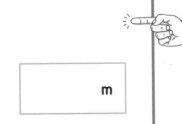

Mass can be measured using grams and kilograms. Lighter objects are measured in grams (g), heavier objects are measured in kilograms (kg).

We can convert between these units:

'kilo' means 'one thousand of'

$$kg \xrightarrow{\times 1,000} g$$
$$kg \xleftarrow{\div 1,000} g$$

e.g. 1 Write 4 kg in grams.

×1,000

kg	g
1	1,000
4	4,000

×1,000

1 Recall ... 1 kg = 1,000 g

2 Multiply by 1,000 to convert kg to g

g are smaller than kg ... expect an answer greater than 4

4 kg = 4,000 g

e.g. 2 Convert 3,500 g to kilograms.

÷1,000

g	kg
1,000	1
3,500	3.5

÷1,000

1 1,000 g = 1 kg

2 Divide by 1,000 to convert g to kg

kg are larger than g ... expect an answer smaller than 3,500

3,500 g = 3.5 kg

Capacity can be measured using millilitres and litres. Smaller amounts are measured in millilitres (ml), larger amounts are measured in litres (l).

We can convert between these units:

$$litre \xrightarrow{\times 1,000} ml$$
$$litre \xleftarrow{\div 1,000} ml$$

'milli' means 'one thousandth of'

e.g. 3 Write 3.25 litres in millilitres.

×1,000

litres	ml
1	1,000
3.25	3,250

×1,000

1 Recall ... 1 litre = 1,000 ml

2 Expect a larger answer ... multiply by 1,000

3.25 litres = 3,250 ml

e.g. 4 Convert 475 ml to litres.

÷1,000

ml	litres
1,000	1
475	0.475

÷1,000

1 1,000 ml = 1 litre

2 Expect a smaller answer ... divide by 1,000

475 ml = 0.475 litres

1,000 millilitres = 1 litre   1,000 grams = 1 kilogram

1 Calculate:

5,000 ÷ 1,000 =   7,500 ÷ 1,000 =

4,025 ÷ 1,000 =   325 ÷ 1,000 =

1.425 x 1,000 =   2.75 x 1,000 =

4.5 x 1,000 =   0.8 x 1,000 =

SET?

A. Complete the table:

kg	g
1	
4	
	3,000
2.5	
	4,500

B. Complete the table:

g	kg
1,200	
2,750	
	3.45
675	
	0.4

C. Complete the table:

litre	ml
1	
3	
	6,000
6.3	
	1,480

D. Complete the table:

ml	litre
1,400	
2,750	
	1.35
720	
	2.045

E. Convert 1.005 kg to grams

F. Write 3,020 ml in litres

 **GO!**

CONVERTING METRIC UNITS 2

1. How many 300 ml cups can be filled from a 1.5 litre bottle?

2. Albie pours 40 millilitres from a half litre bottle of milk. He says,

"I have 10 millilitres of milk left".

Do you agree? Explain your answer.

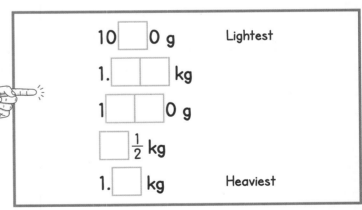

3. A bag contains 2.6 kg of soil.

Dawson uses all the soil in the bag to fill some plant pots.

Each plant pot holds 200 grams of soil.

How many plant pots does Dawson fill?

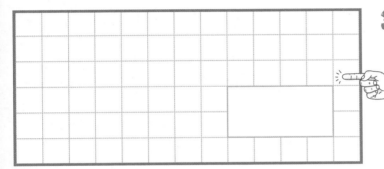

4. Kelvin weighs some books.

He puts the masses of the books in order from lightest to heaviest.

Use the digits 0, 1, 2, 3, 4, 5 and 6 once each to complete the list.

10 ☐ 0 g	Lightest
1. ☐ ☐ kg	
1 ☐ ☐ 0 g	
☐ $\frac{1}{2}$ kg	
1. ☐ kg	Heaviest

5. 150 millilitres of water flows from a tap every second.

How many litres of water will flow from the tap in one minute?

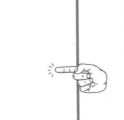

READY?

Polygons are 2D shapes with straight sides ...

Triangles are polygons with three sides. Triangles have one of these three properties:

All sides equal
Equilateral

Two sides equal
Isosceles

No sides equal
Scalene

Quadrilaterals are polygons with four sides:

Rectangle Square Parallelogram Rhombus Trapezium Kite

Regular polygons have the special property that all sides are equal and all angles are equal:

Triangle Square Pentagon Hexagon Heptagon Octagon

e.g. 1 Tick the polygons with at least one pair of parallel sides.

Parallel sides are always the same distance apart

CHECK-IN

1. Tick all the pairs of parallel lines:

2. Tick all the pairs of perpendicular lines:

3. Label the right angles R, acute angles A, and obtuse angles O

Ready for take off?

e.g. 2 Tick the polygons that have at least one pair of perpendicular sides.

Perpendicular sides meet at right angles

We can compare using other properties:

e.g. 3 Tick the pentagons with two or more obtuse angles.

5 sides → pentagon
All angles are obtuse

5 sides → pentagon
Two angles are obtuse

5 sides → pentagon
No obtuse angles

6 sides → hexagon
(not a pentagon!)

Obtuse angles are more than 90° and less than 180°

6 sides → hexagon
(again, not a pentagon!)

A. Tick the polygons with at least one right angle:

C. Tick the polygons that are regular:

SET?

B. Place the names of the shapes in the correct place in the table:

	No parallel sides	Has parallel sides
No right angles		
One or more right angles		

Right-angled triangle

Square

Regular hexagon

Regular pentagon

D. Place the names of the shapes in the correct place in the diagram:

Two acute angles

Quadrilateral

GO!

2D SHAPES

1. This trapezium has diagonals that cross at right angles:

Tick the quadrilaterals with diagonals that cross at right angles.

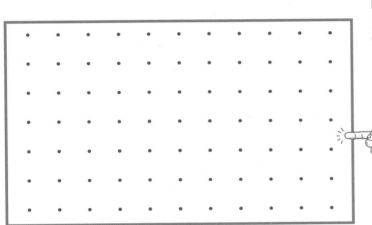

2. Use the dotted grid to draw an octagon with at least four acute angles.

3. Complete the diagram by writing the name of a shape in the empty boxes.

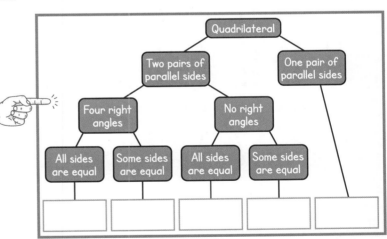

4. Complete the table by writing the name of a shape in each position.

	Has parallel sides	No parallel sides
Regular		
Irregular		

HINT: Irregular = not regular

READY?

If we fold a shape into two sections and the two sections match exactly, we say that the shape has a **line of symmetry**.

For example, if this rectangle is folded along the dotted line the two sections will match:

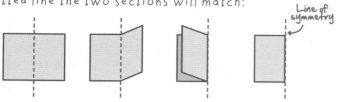

Line of symmetry

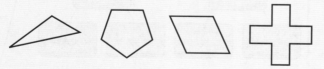

Line symmetry is sometimes called reflective symmetry

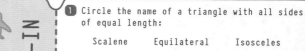

JUSTAROO Airlines

CHECK-IN

Ready for take off?

1 Circle the name of a triangle with all sides of equal length:

Scalene   Equilateral   Isosceles

True or false?
2 A rectangle is a regular polygon
3 A pentagon has six sides
4 An octagon has eight sides

e.g. 1 Tick the shapes with reflective symmetry.

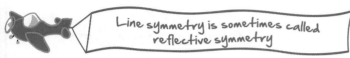

How can I fold the shapes in half?

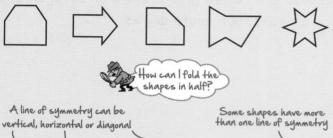

A line of symmetry can be vertical, horizontal or diagonal

Some shapes have more than one line of symmetry

Some shapes have no lines of symmetry

e.g. 2 How many lines of symmetry does a rectangle have?

These two sections match ...

... and so do these two sections

A rectangle has 2 lines of symmetry

There is NOT a diagonal line of symmetry

e.g. 3 How many lines of symmetry does a square have?

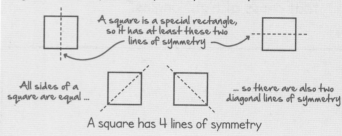

A square is a special rectangle, so it has at least these two lines of symmetry

All sides of a square are equal ...

... so there are also two diagonal lines of symmetry

A square has 4 lines of symmetry

e.g. 4 How many lines of symmetry does an equilateral triangle have?

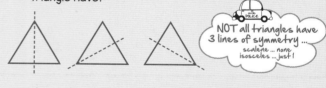

NOT all triangles have 3 lines of symmetry ...
scalene ... none
isosceles ... just 1

An equilateral triangle has 3 lines of symmetry

A. Tick the polygons with reflective symmetry.

SET?

B. How many lines of symmetry does each of the quadrilaterals have?

(i)

(ii)

(iii)

(iv)

C. How many lines of symmetry does a regular hexagon have?

D. Join dots to make an octagon with one line of symmetry.

124

1. Shade the smallest possible number of squares to complete the diagram with two lines of symmetry.

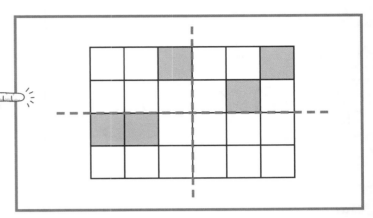

2. Denise thinks that this parallelogram has two lines of symmetry.

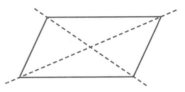

Do you agree with Denise? Explain why.

3. Complete the table by writing the name of a shape in each position.

	No lines of symmetry	Two lines of symmetry
No right angles		
At least two right angles		

4. Create a shape with one line of symmetry using all the shapes below:

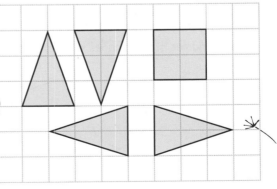

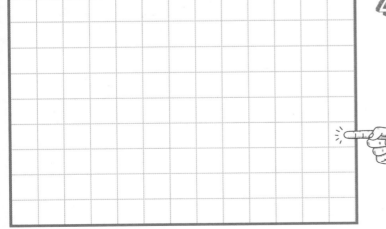

READY?

3D shapes have surfaces ... the surfaces can be either flat or curved.

Some 3D shapes just have flat surfaces: e.g. **cuboid**.
Some just have curved surfaces: e.g. **sphere**.
Others have a mixture of flat and curved surfaces:
e.g. **cone** or **cylinder**.

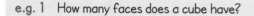

There are special words for parts of a 3D shape:

Face - a flat surface
Edge - where two faces meet
Vertex - where edges meet

e.g. 1   How many faces does a cube have?

Front and back:
two faces

Side and side:
two faces

Top and bottom:
two faces

$2 + 2 + 2 = 6$

A cube has six faces

CHECK-IN
JUSTAROO Airlines

Ready for take off?

1 Tick all the prisms:

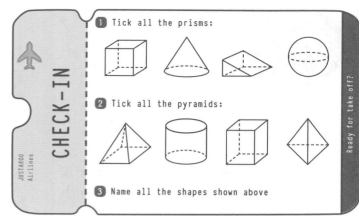

2 Tick all the pyramids:

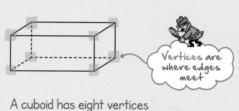

3 Name all the shapes shown above

The plural of 'vertex' is 'vertices':

e.g. 2   How many vertices does a cuboid have?

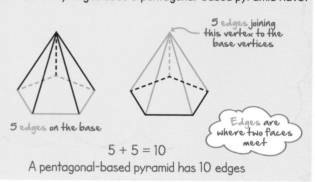

Vertices are where edges meet

A cuboid has eight vertices

e.g. 3   How many edges does a pentagonal-based pyramid have?

5 edges joining this vertex to the base vertices

5 edges on the base

Edges are where two faces meet

$5 + 5 = 10$

A pentagonal-based pyramid has 10 edges

SET?

A. Complete the table:

3D shape	Number of faces	Number of edges	Number of vertices
Triangular prism			
Triangular-based pyramid			
Square-based pyramid			
Hexagonal prism			
Hexagonal-based pyramid			

B. Place the names of the shapes in the correct place in the diagram:

Has flat faces

Has curved faces

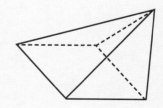

Cylinder

Sphere

Triangular prism

C. Circle the vertex where the greatest number of edges meet.

3D SHAPES 1

1. Name two different 3D shapes with seven faces.

2. Complete the table by writing the name of a 3D shape in each position.

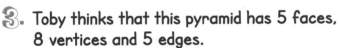

	Even number of faces	Odd number of faces
Even number of edges		
Even number of vertices		

3. Toby thinks that this pyramid has 5 faces, 8 vertices and 5 edges.

Do you agree? Explain your answer.

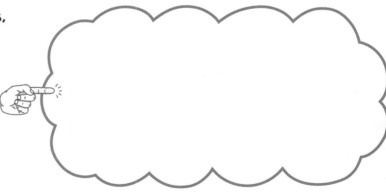

4. Always true / Sometimes true / Never true:

A pyramid has the same number of vertices as faces.

Explain your answer.

Imagine a box of cereal ... and unfold it!

This is a cuboid   This is a **net** of a cuboid

 A net is a 2D representation of a 3D shape

CHECK-IN
JUSTAROO Airlines

Ready for take off?

True or false?
1 All the faces of a triangular prism are triangles
2 All the faces of a triangular-based pyramid are triangles
3 All the faces of a square-based pyramid are square
4 All the faces of a cube are square

e.g. 2 Here is the net of a 3D shape. Name the shape.

The net is made from four 2D shapes, so the 3D shape has four faces

Each of the 4 shapes is an equilateral triangle, so all faces of the 3D shape are equilateral triangles

Pick one shape as the base and visualise folding the net up

The shape is a triangular-based pyramid (also called a tetrahedron)

e.g. 1 Here is the net of a 3D shape. Name the shape.

The net is made from six 2D shapes, so the 3D shape has six faces

Each of the 6 shapes is a square, so all faces of the 3D shape are a square

Pick one shape as the base and visualise folding the net up

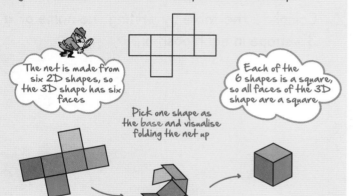

The shape is a cube

e.g. 3 Draw the net of this 3D shape.

The 3D shape has five faces, so the net is made from five 2D shapes

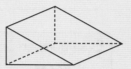

2 faces are triangular

3 faces are rectangular

Visualise unfolding the shape

These two lines are the same length ...

... and so are these two lines

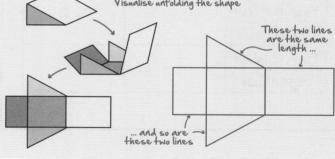

A. Tick the nets of a cube:

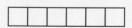

B. Here are the nets of two 3D shapes. Name the shapes.

(i)
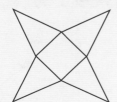

(ii)
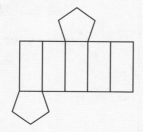

C. Here is a cuboid.
Draw a net of the cuboid.

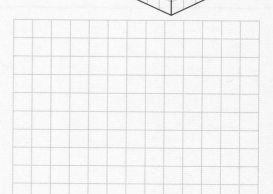

1. Kay is drawing the net of a hexagonal prism.

List all the 2D shapes that make up the net.

2. Sophie thinks she has drawn a net of a triangular-based pyramid:

Do you agree? Explain your answer.

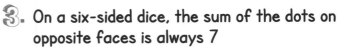

3. On a six-sided dice, the sum of the dots on opposite faces is always 7

Draw numbers on the three empty faces of the net so that it folds up to make a dice.

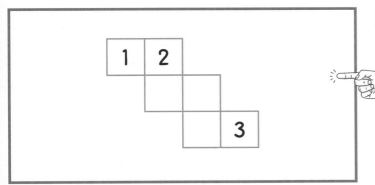

4. Tonia has drawn a net of a shape.

She has used 2 squares and 4 identical rectangles.

Name the 3D shape.

5. Brett has drawn a net of a pyramid.

He has used 5 identical triangles and one other polygon.

Name the other polygon.

READY?

Perimeter is the total distance around a shape.

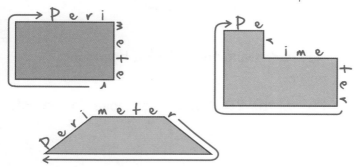

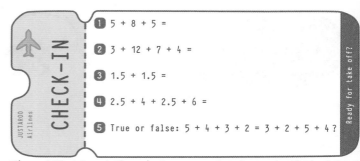

JUSTAROO Airlines

CHECK-IN

1. 5 + 8 + 5 =
2. 3 + 12 + 7 + 4 =
3. 1.5 + 1.5 =
4. 2.5 + 4 + 2.5 + 6 =
5. True or false: 5 + 4 + 3 + 2 = 3 + 2 + 5 + 4?

Ready for take off?

e.g. 1 A square is drawn on a centimetre grid. Find the perimeter of the square.

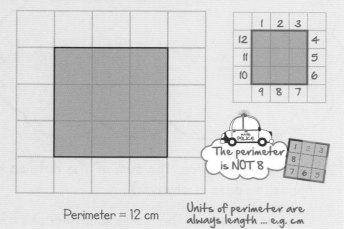

Perimeter = 12 cm

The perimeter is NOT 8

Units of perimeter are always length ... e.g. cm

The perimeter of a shape can also be calculated ...

e.g. 2 Calculate the perimeter of the trapezium.

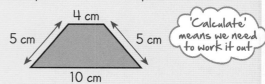

4 cm

5 cm   5 cm

10 cm

'Calculate' means we need to work it out

The perimeter is the TOTAL distance around the shape

Perimeter = 4 + 5 + 10 + 5
= 24 cm

Sometimes not all the lengths of the sides are given.

e.g. 3 Calculate the perimeter of the shape.

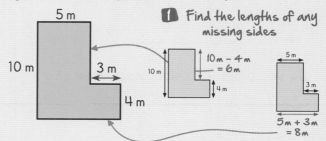

5 m
10 m   3 m
4 m

1 Find the lengths of any missing sides

10m – 4m = 6m

5m + 3m = 8m

2 Calculate the perimeter by adding up all the sides

Perimeter = 10 + 5 + 6 + 3 + 4 + 8
= 36 m

Perimeter is the TOTAL distance around a shape

SET!

A. Some shapes are drawn on a centimetre grid. Find the perimeter of each shape.

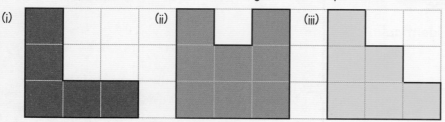

(i)   (ii)   (iii)

B. Calculate the perimeter of these shapes.

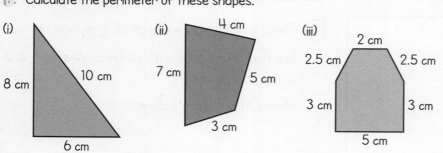

(i)
8 cm   10 cm
6 cm

(ii)
4 cm
7 cm   5 cm
3 cm

(iii)
2 cm
2.5 cm   2.5 cm
3 cm   3 cm
5 cm

C. Calculate the perimeter of these shapes.

(i)
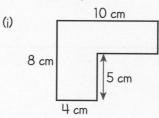
10 cm
8 cm
5 cm
4 cm

(ii)
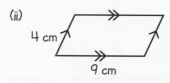
4 cm
9 cm

130

PERIMETER

1. A regular hexagon has a perimeter of 54 cm.

Calculate the length of a side of the hexagon.

2. Toni thinks the perimeter of the rectangle is 13 centimetres.

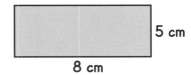

5 cm

8 cm

Explain why Toni is not correct.

3. Tick the shape with the longest perimeter.

A square with side length 6 cm ☐

A regular pentagon with side length 5 cm ☐

Explain how you know.

4. Jo is putting ribbon around the edge of her flag. The flag is a rectangle with an equilateral triangle on the end.

50 cm

75 cm

The ribbon costs £2.50 per metre.

How much does the ribbon cost?

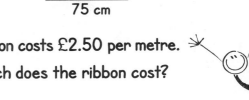

REMEMBER: 100 cm = 1 m

READY?

Area measures the amount of space inside an enclosed shape.

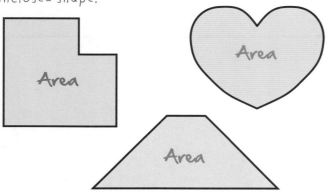

The area of a shape can be found by counting squares.

e.g. 1 Find the area of this shape.

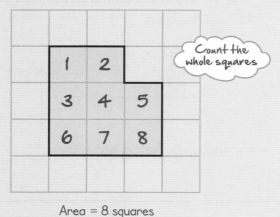

Count the whole squares

Area = 8 squares

JUSTAROO Airlines

CHECK-IN

Ready for take off?

1 Calculate:
$\frac{1}{2} + \frac{1}{2} =$ $\frac{1}{2} + \frac{1}{2} + \frac{1}{2} + \frac{1}{2} =$

2 Tick the squares that have more than half shaded:

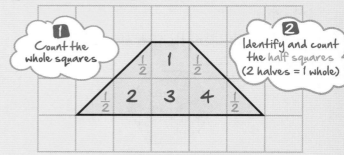

We can also find the area of shapes that do not just have whole squares ...

e.g. 2 Find the area of this trapezium.

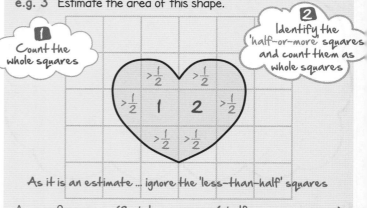

1 Count the whole squares

2 Identify and count the half squares (2 halves = 1 whole)

Area = 6 squares (4 whole squares + 4 half squares)

We can estimate areas of other irregular shapes ...

e.g. 3 Estimate the area of this shape.

1 Count the whole squares

2 Identify the 'half-or-more' squares and count them as whole squares

As it is an estimate ... ignore the 'less-than-half' squares

Area = 8 squares (2 whole squares + 6 half-or-more squares)

A. Find the area of these shapes.

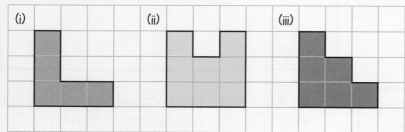

(i)   (ii)   (iii)

SET?

B. Find the area of these shapes.

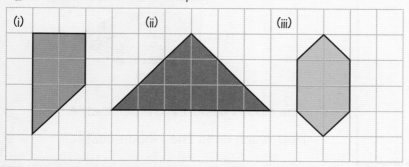

(i)   (ii)   (iii)

C. Estimate the area of these shapes.

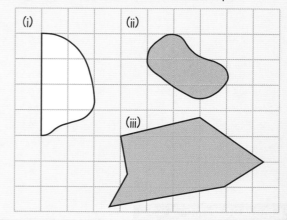

(i)   (ii)

(iii)

AREA

1. Draw three different rectangles with an area of 12 squares.

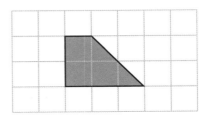

2. Penny thinks that the area of this shape is 5 squares.

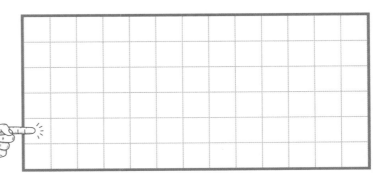

Do you agree? Explain your answer.

3. Here is a picture of a leaf.

   Estimate the area.

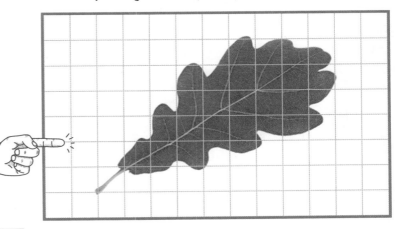

4. a) Match the shape with its area.

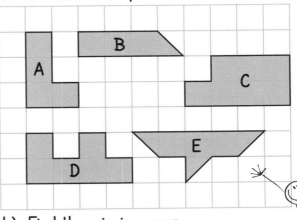

Shape	Area
A	$3\frac{1}{2}$ squares
B	4 squares
C	
D	4.5 squares
E	6 squares

b) Find the missing area.

READY?

The area of this rectangle can be found by counting squares:

1	2	3	4	5
6	7	8	9	10
11	12	13	14	15

3 cm

5 cm

Area of rectangle = 15 square centimetres = 15 cm²

The area of the rectangle can also be **calculated** by thinking about the five centimetre squares repeated 3 times (or three centimetre squares repeated 5 times!)

Area = 5 × 3 = 15 cm²

Area of a rectangle = length × width

e.g. 1 Calculate the area of the rectangle.

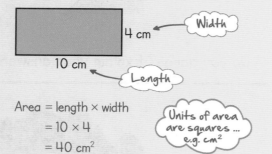

4 cm — Width

10 cm — Length

Area = length × width
= 10 × 4
= 40 cm²

Units of area are squares ... e.g. cm²

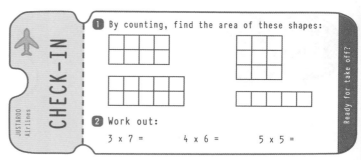

JUSTAROO Airlines

CHECK-IN

Ready for take off?

1. By counting, find the area of these shapes:

2. Work out:

3 × 7 =   4 × 6 =   5 × 5 =

A square is a special rectangle ... so we can also calculate the area of a square:

e.g. 2 Find the area of the square.

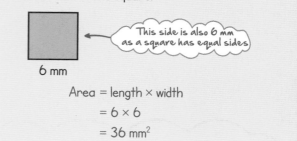

6 mm

This side is also 6 mm as a square has equal sides

Area = length × width
= 6 × 6
= 36 mm²

We can also find a missing length of a rectangle if we are given the area:

e.g. 3 The area of a rectangle is 24 cm². The width of the rectangle is 3 cm.

Area = 24 cm²   3 cm

Calculate the length of the rectangle.

Area = length × width
24 = length × 3
24 ÷ 3 = length
Length = 8 cm

The units of length here are centimetres

A. Calculate the area of these rectangles.

(i)
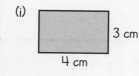
3 cm
4 cm

(ii)
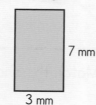
7 mm
3 mm

(iii)
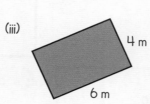
4 m
6 m

SET?

B. Find the area of these squares.

(i)
3 cm

(ii)
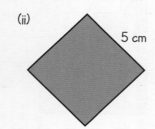
5 cm

C. Complete the table (all dimensions are whole numbers).

Width	Length	Area
5 cm		40 cm²
	6 m	24 m²
4 cm		36 cm²
		17 mm²

1. The area of a square is between 70 cm^2 and 95 cm^2.

The length of the square is a whole number.

Find the length of the square.

2. Max thinks the area of the rectangle is:

$4 + 11 + 4 + 11 = 30$ cm

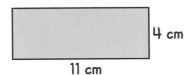

4 cm

11 cm

Do you agree with Max? Explain why.

3. Always true / Sometimes true / Never true:

The value of the area of a rectangle is greater than the value of the perimeter of the rectangle

Explain your answer.

4. The area of a rectangle is 60 cm^2.

The dimensions of the rectangle are whole numbers.

Find the dimensions of four different rectangles with this area.

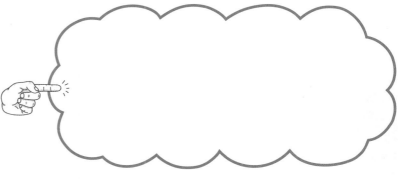

☐ and ☐   ☐ and ☐

☐ and ☐   ☐ and ☐

5. A picture frame is made by removing a small rectangle from a larger rectangle.

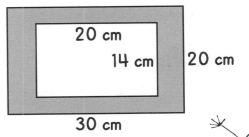

20 cm

14 cm   20 cm

30 cm

Find the area of the picture frame.

READY?

Two identical triangles will always make a rectangle.
Sometimes the second triangle needs cutting into parts:

 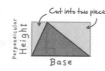 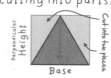

The area of each rectangle can be found by multiplying the **base** of the triangle by the **perpendicular height** of the triangle. Since two triangles are used to make each rectangle:

$$\text{Area of triangle} = \frac{1}{2} \times \text{area of rectangle}$$

$$\text{Area of triangle} = \frac{1}{2} \times \textbf{base} \times \textbf{perpendicular height}$$

All these triangles have the same area as they have the same base length and the same perpendicular height:

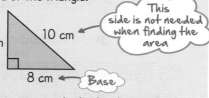

e.g. 1   Calculate the area of the triangle.

Perpendicular height → 6 cm   *10 cm — This side is not needed when finding the area*   *8 cm ← Base*

Area = $\frac{1}{2}$ × base × perpendicular height

= $\frac{1}{2}$ × 8 × 6   8×6=48

= 24 cm² $\frac{1}{2}$ of 48 = 24

Base × height is for rectangles ... NOT triangles

CHECK-IN

JUSTAR00 Airlines

Ready for take off?

1 Tick all the pairs of perpendicular lines:

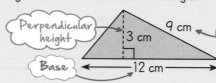

2 $\frac{1}{2}$ of 26 =   3 $\frac{1}{2}$ of 70 =

4 True or false?

$\frac{1}{2}$ of 8 × 12 = 4 × 12 = 8 × 6

Not all triangles are right-angled triangles ...

e.g. 2   Find the area of the triangle.

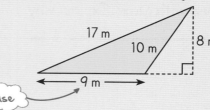

Perpendicular height   *3 cm*   *9 cm — The 9cm length is not needed when finding the area*   *Base — 12 cm*

Area = $\frac{1}{2}$ × base × perpendicular height

= $\frac{1}{2}$ × 12 × 3   12×3=36

= 18 cm² $\frac{1}{2}$ of 36 = 18

or ... $\frac{1}{2}$ of 12 = 6, 6×3 = 18

or ... $\frac{1}{2}$ of 3 = 1.5, 1.5×12 = 18

Sometimes the perpendicular height is 'outside' the triangle.

e.g. 3   Calculate the area of the triangle.

17 m   *10 m*   *8 m*   *Perpendicular height*   *9 m*   *Base*

Area = $\frac{1}{2}$ × base × perpendicular height

= $\frac{1}{2}$ × 9 × 8   9×8=72

= 36 m² $\frac{1}{2}$ of 72 = 36

SET?

A. Calculate the area of these triangles.

(i)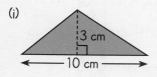
3 cm, 4 cm

(ii)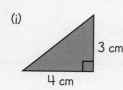
14 mm, 5 mm

(iii)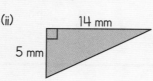
9 m, 15 m, 12 m

B. Find the area of these triangles.

(i) 3 cm, 10 cm

(ii) 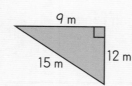 4 cm, 7 cm, 11 cm

(iii) 12 m, 5 m, 10 m

C. Calculate the area of these triangles.

(i)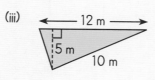
12 m, 13 m, 15 m, 4 m

(ii)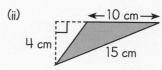
10 cm, 4 cm, 15 cm

GO!

AREA OF TRIANGLES

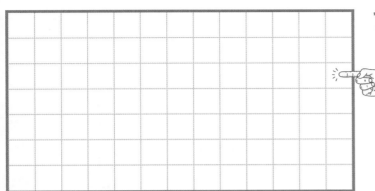

1. Draw two different triangles with an area of 6 squares.

2. The area of this triangle is 30 cm²

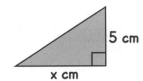

5 cm

x cm

Find the value of x.

3. The triangle has the same area as a square.

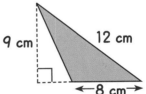

9 cm

12 cm

8 cm

Find the length of a side of the square.

4. Ray is finding the area of this triangle:

He writes:

$$\text{Area} = \frac{1}{2} \times 5 \times 4 = 10 \text{ cm}^2$$

Do you agree? Explain your answer.

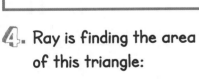

8 cm   4 cm

5 cm

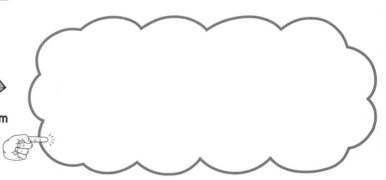

5. Find the area of the pentagon.

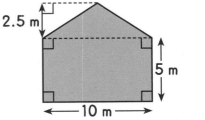

2.5 m

5 m

10 m

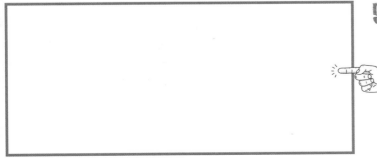

READY?

Compound shapes are shapes that are made up of two or more simple shapes.

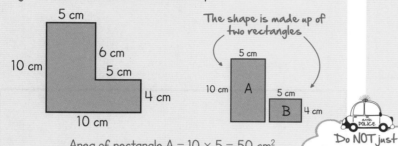

The area of compound shapes can be found by splitting the shape into simple shapes:

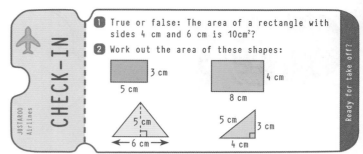

CHECK-IN

JUSTAROO Airlines

Ready for take off?

1. True or false: The area of a rectangle with sides 4 cm and 6 cm is 10cm²?
2. Work out the area of these shapes:

3 cm
5 cm

4 cm
8 cm

5 cm
6 cm

5 cm
3 cm
4 cm

e.g. 1   Calculate the area of this shape.

The shape is made up of two rectangles

5 cm

6 cm
10 cm
5 cm
4 cm
10 cm

5 cm
10 cm   A   5 cm
B   4 cm

Area of rectangle A = 10 × 5 = 50 cm²

Area of rectangle B = 5 × 4 = 20 cm²

Area of shape = Area of rectangle A + Area of rectangle B
= 50 + 20
= 70 cm²

OR   The shape could also be split into these two rectangles

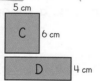

5 cm
C   6 cm
D   4 cm
10 cm

Area of rectangle C = 6 × 5 = 30 cm²

Area of rectangle D = 10 × 4 = 40 cm²

Area of shape = 30 + 40
= 70 cm²

Do NOT just multiply all the numbers together

We can also find the area of compound shapes when the lengths of some of the sides are not given:

e.g. 2   Find the area of this shape.

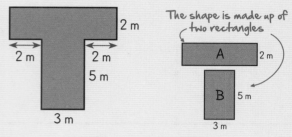

2 m
2 m   2 m
5 m
3 m

The shape is made up of two rectangles

A   2 m
B   5 m
3 m

Area of rectangle B = 5 × 3 = 15 m²

The length of rectangle A has not been given ...

A   2 m

... but it can be calculated using the other sides:

A   2 m
2 m   3 m   2 m

2m + 3m + 2m = 7m

Area of rectangle A = 7 × 2 = 14 m²

Area of shape = Area of rectangle A + Area of rectangle B
= 14 + 15
= 29 m²

A. Calculate the area of these shapes.

(i)
4 cm
8 cm
5 cm
4 cm
3 cm
8 cm

(ii)
10 cm
5 cm
3 cm
9 cm
4 cm
7 cm

(iii)
12 m
5 m   1 m   5 m
9 m
2 m

SET?

B. Calculate the perimeter of these shapes.

(i)
8 cm
2 cm
4 cm
5 cm

(ii)
12 m
9 m   6 m
8 m

(iii)
2 cm
2 cm
10 cm
9 cm
5 cm

GO!

AREA OF COMPOUND SHAPES

1. Calculate the area of this shape.

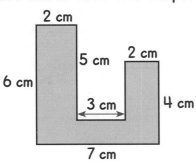

2 cm

5 cm

6 cm

2 cm

3 cm

4 cm

7 cm

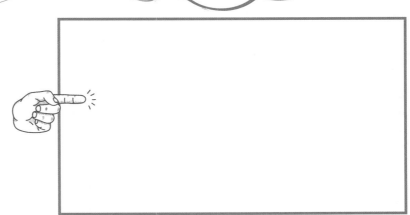

2. The area of this shape is 60 cm²

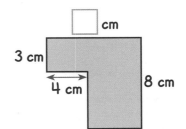

☐ cm

3 cm

4 cm

8 cm

Find the length of the missing side.

3. Carson calculates the area of this shape as:

$7 \times 6 \times 2 \times 1 = 84$ cm²

Do you agree with Carson?

Explain your answer.

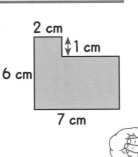

2 cm

1 cm

6 cm

7 cm

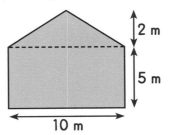

4. Blake is painting the side of his house.

2 m

5 m

10 m

One litre of paint covers 12 m².

How many litres of paint does Blake need?

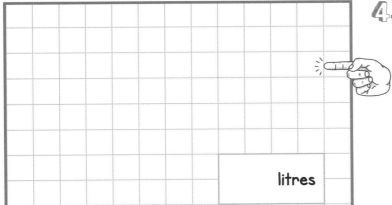

litres

A ruler and a protractor (and a pencil) are used to draw accurate diagrams.

A ruler is used to measure and draw lengths. For example, this line is 5 cm long:

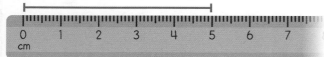

A protractor is used to measure and draw angles. Most protractors have two scales (for measuring in each direction). We must be careful to use the correct scale. For example, this angle is 40°, not 140°.

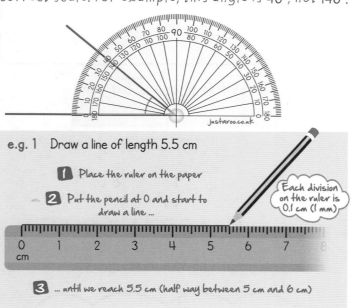

e.g. 1 Draw a line of length 5.5 cm

1 Place the ruler on the paper

2 Put the pencil at 0 and start to draw a line ...

Each division on the ruler is 0.1 cm (1 mm)

3 ... until we reach 5.5 cm (half way between 5 cm and 6 cm)

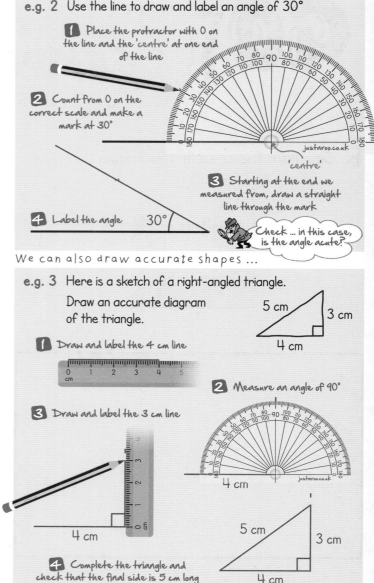

e.g. 2 Use the line to draw and label an angle of 30°

1 Place the protractor with 0 on the line and the 'centre' at one end of the line

2 Count from 0 on the correct scale and make a mark at 30°

3 Starting at the end we measured from, draw a straight line through the mark

4 Label the angle 30°

Check ... in this case, is the angle acute?

We can also draw accurate shapes ...

e.g. 3 Here is a sketch of a right-angled triangle. Draw an accurate diagram of the triangle.

5 cm   3 cm   4 cm

1 Draw and label the 4 cm line

2 Measure an angle of 90°

3 Draw and label the 3 cm line

4 cm   4 cm

4 Complete the triangle and check that the final side is 5 cm long

5 cm   3 cm   4 cm

Complete A, B and C on a piece of plain paper

A. Draw a line of length:

(i) 3 cm

(ii) 16 cm

(iii) 8.5 cm

(iv) 11.3 cm

B. Draw and label an angle of:

(i) 50°

(ii) 65°

(iii) 15°

(iv) 150°

(v) 165°

HINT: Draw any line to get started with B

C. Here is a sketch of a right-angled triangle.

(i) Draw an accurate diagram of the triangle.

(ii) Measure the length of the longest side.

7 cm   3 cm

D. Draw an isosceles triangle with two angles of 35°. The base has been drawn for you.

A ——————— B
     7 cm

DRAWING LINES, ANGLES AND SHAPES

1. Draw an accurate diagram of an equilateral triangle with side length 3 centimetres.

2. James thinks he has drawn an angle of 135°

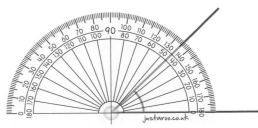

Is James correct? Explain how you know.

3. Ian has made a sketch of a shape:

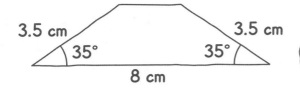

Draw an accurate diagram of his shape.

4. Find the length of the diagonal of a square with side length 4 centimetres.

READY?

There are facts about angles that we need to know:

The sum of the angles around a point is 360°

120° 180° 60°
$90° + 90° + 90° + 90° = 360°$
100° 100° 160°

$180° + 120° + 60° = 360°$

Right angle = 90°

$100° + 100° + 160° = 360°$

Angle facts can be used to solve problems ...

e.g. 1   Calculate the size of the angle labelled x.

x 140°

The angles are around a point ... so the total of the angles is 360°

$$360° - 140° = 220°$$
$$x = 220°$$

'Calculate' means work out the missing angle using facts ... the diagram is not drawn to scale, so the angle should NOT be measured

CHECK-IN

JUSTAROO Airlines

1 How many right angles make a whole turn?

2 Work out:

170 + 110 =   130 + 25 =

95 + 105 =   90 + 25 + 35 =

360 − 100 =   360 − 120 =

360 − 280 =   360 − 305 =

Ready for take off?

Sometimes problems involve more than two angles:

e.g. 2   Calculate the size of the angle labelled y.

120° 80° y

1 Identify that all three angles are around a point and must add up to 360°

2 Find the total of the known angles:
$$120° + 80° = 200°$$

3 Find the value of y:
$$360° - 200° = 160°$$
$$y = 160°$$

Sometimes problems involve right angles:

e.g. 3   Calculate the size of the angle labelled x.

x 100° 40° 90°

All four angles are around a point ... so the total of the angles is 360°

$$100° + 40° + 90° = 230°$$
$$360° - 230° = 130°$$
$$x = 130°$$

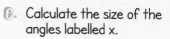

A. Calculate the size of the angles labelled x.

(i)
x 100°

(ii)
x 205°

(iii)
315° x

SET?

B. Calculate the size of the angles labelled y.

(i)
170° 110° y

(ii)
25° y 130°

(iii)
160° 85° 85° y

C. Calculate the size of the angles labelled x.

(i)
105° x 95°

(ii)
25° x 35°

ANGLES AT A POINT

Cracking!

1. Find the value of b.

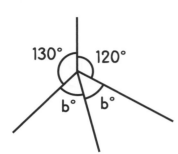

130° 120°

b° b°

2. Use the digits 1, 2, 3 and 4 to find the missing angles.

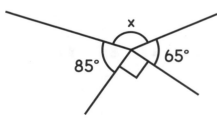

☐0°

☐0° 80°

☐☐0°

3. Avery thinks the size of the missing angle labelled x cannot be found because she only has information about two of the angles.

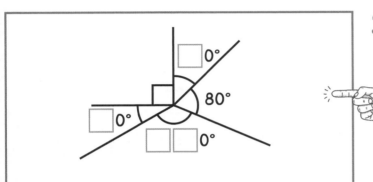

x

85° 65°

Do you agree? Explain your answer.

4. ABCDEF is a regular hexagon.

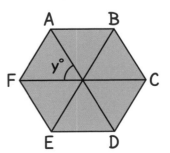

A   B

F   y°   C

E   D

Find the size of angle y.

READY?

We can use the fact that

the sum of the angles around a point is 360°

to find other facts. For example, if there are 360° in a full turn, there must be 180° in half a turn.

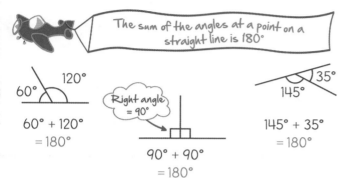

The sum of the angles at a point on a straight line is 180°

60° 120°

60° + 120°
= 180°

Right angle = 90°

90° + 90°
= 180°

145° 35°

145° + 35°
= 180°

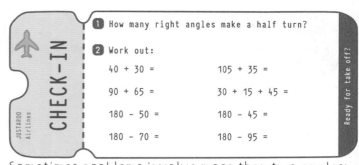

e.g. 1 Calculate the size of the angle labelled x.

80° x

The angles are at a point on a straight line ... so the total of the angles is 180°

180° − 80° = 100°
x = 100°

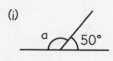
Do NOT try to measure the angles ... 'calculate' means 'work out'

Sometimes problems involve more than two angles:

e.g. 2 Calculate the size of the angle labelled y.

1 Identify that all three angles are at a point on a straight line and must add up to 180°

30°
y
40°

The straight line can be horizontal or vertical

2 Find the total of the known angles:
40° + 30° = 70°

3 Find the value of y:
180° − 70° = 110°
y = 110°

Sometimes problems involve right angles:

e.g. 3 Calculate the size of the angle labelled b.

Right angle = 90°

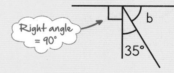
b
35°

Even though the angles are below the line, they still meet at a point

35° + 90° = 125°
180° − 125° = 55°
b = 55°

A. Calculate the size of the labelled angles.

(i)
a 50°

(ii)
b
45°

(iii)
c 115°

SET?

B. Calculate the size of the labelled angles.

(i)
40° a 20°

(ii)
105°
35°
b

(iii)
55°
c 45°

C. Calculate the size of the labelled angles.

(i)
20°
a

(ii)
b 65°

1. Find the value of a.

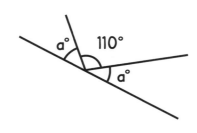

2. Four different angles meet at a point on a straight line.

Use the digits 3, 4, 5 and 6 to find the size of the three missing angles.

3. Dhruv thinks that the size of angle x is 40° because angles on a straight line add up to 180°.

Do you agree? Explain why.

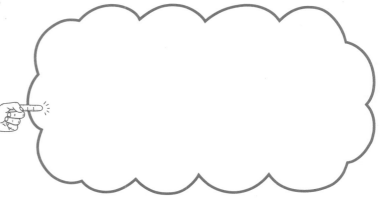

4. Five angles meet at a point on a straight line.

Alix thinks that all five angles must be acute angles.

Do you agree? Explain your answer.

READY?

We can use the fact that **the sum of the angles at a point on a straight line is 180°** to discover facts about angles in triangles.

We can make a tiling pattern with any triangle ...

... and the 3 angles always meet at a point on a line:

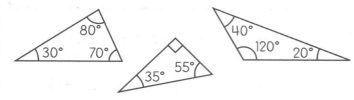

So ● + ● + ● = 180°

The sum of the angles in any triangle is 180°

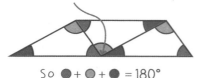

e.g. 1 Calculate the size of the angle labelled x.

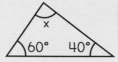

1 Identify that the three angles are in a triangle and must add up to 180°

2 Find the total of the known angles: 60° + 40° = 100°

3 Find the value of x: 180° − 100° = 80°

x = 80°

CHECK-IN

1 Circle the obtuse angles:
   60°   100°   150°   250°

2 Circle the name of a triangle with two sides of equal length:
   Scalene   Equilateral   Isosceles

3 80 ÷ 2 =   **4** 130 ÷ 2 =

Ready for take off?

Sometimes problems involve special types of triangles, such as right-angled triangles ...

e.g. 2 Calculate the size of the angle labelled y.

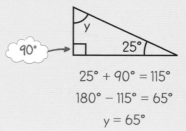

25° + 90° = 115°

180° − 115° = 65°

y = 65°

... or isosceles triangles:

e.g. 3 Calculate the size of the angle labelled x.

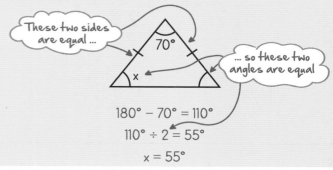

These two sides are equal ...   ... so these two angles are equal

180° − 70° = 110°

110° ÷ 2 = 55°

x = 55°

The sum of the angles in a triangle is 180°

A. Calculate the size of the labelled angles.

(i)
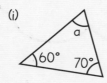

(ii)
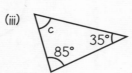

(iii)

SET?

C. Calculate the size of the angle labelled x.

(i)
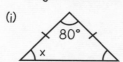

B. Calculate the size of the labelled angles.

(i)
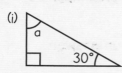

(ii)
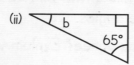

(iii)
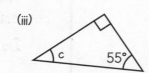

(ii)
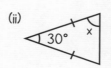

(iii)

146

 **GO!**

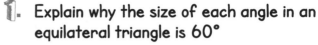 # ANGLES IN A TRIANGLE

Bostin!

---

1. Explain why the size of each angle in an equilateral triangle is 60°

---

2. Jordan thinks that the size of the angle labelled x in this isosceles triangle is 40°

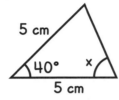

5 cm
40°   x
5 cm

Do you agree with Jordan? Explain why.

x = ⬚ °

3. Calculate the size of the angle labelled x.

x
50°   115°

---

4. Angie thinks that a triangle can have two obtuse angles.

Explain why Angie is not correct.

---

5. The line from X to Y is a straight line.

Calculate the size of the angles labelled a and b.

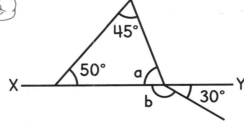

45°
50°   a
X ——————— Y
b   30°

a = ⬚ °

b = ⬚ °

READY?

The position of a point on a grid can be described using **coordinates** (x,y)

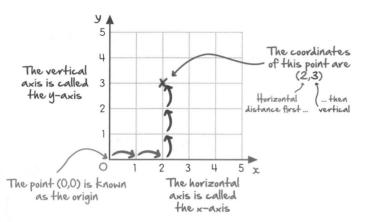

The vertical axis is called the y-axis

The coordinates of this point are (2,3)

Horizontal distance first ... ... then vertical

The point (0,0) is known as the origin

The horizontal axis is called the x-axis

e.g. 1 Write down the coordinates of point P.

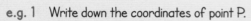

Horizontal distance first! The coordinates are not (2,4)

The coordinates of point P are (4,2)

(x,y) ... horizontal distance, vertical distance

1 Label all the horizontal lines H and all the vertical lines V:

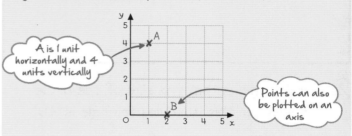

We also need to be able to plot points:

e.g. 2 Plot and label the points A (1,4) and B (2,0)

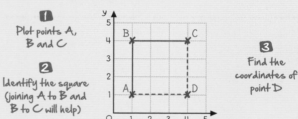

A is 1 unit horizontally and 4 units vertically

Points can also be plotted on an axis

Coordinates can be used to solve problems:

e.g. 3 ABCD is a square
A is the point (1,1)
B is the point (1,4)
C is the point (4,4)
Find the coordinates of point D

1 Plot points A, B and C

2 Identify the square (joining A to B and B to C will help)

3 Find the coordinates of point D

The coordinates of point D are (4,1)

A. Here are four points on a grid.

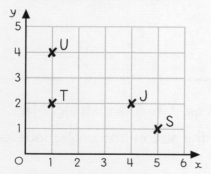

Write down the coordinates of point:

(i) J

(ii) U

(iii) S

(iv) T

B. Plot and label the points.

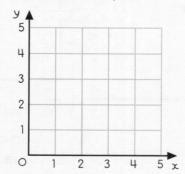

(i) A (5,4)

(ii) R (1,0)

(iii) O (0,3)

(iv) K (1,2)

SET?

C. ABCD is a rectangle.
A is the point (2,0)
B is the point (2,5)
C is the point (5,5)
Find the coordinates of point D.

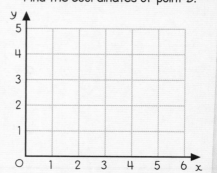

1. Jude thinks the coordinates of point A are (3,4).

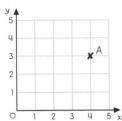

Do you agree? Explain your answer.

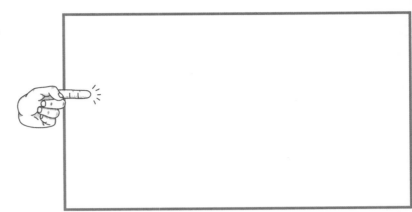

2. A is the point (1,1)
B is the point (2.5,5)
C is the point (4,1)

Nic thinks shape ABC is an equilateral triangle.

Do you agree? Explain your answer.

3. A straight line joins the points P (2,0) and Q (4,4).

What are the coordinates of the midpoint of the line?

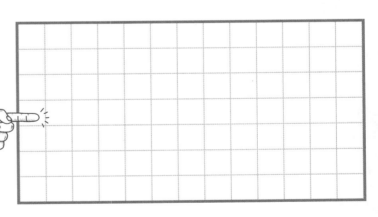

4. Tick all the points that lie on the same horizontal line.

☐	(2,3)
☐	(1,2)
☐	(4,3)
☐	(0,3)
☐	(3,4)

READY?

The x-axis and the y-axis can both be extended beyond zero to include negative numbers.

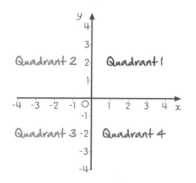

Quadrant 2 Quadrant 1
Quadrant 3 Quadrant 4

Coordinates can be used in all **four quadrants**.

e.g. 1 Plot and label the points P (–3,2) and Q (2,–4)

Point P is 3 units horizontally (to the left since it is negative 3) and 2 units vertically (up since it is positive 2)

Point Q is 2 units horizontally (to the right since it is positive 2) and 4 units vertically (down since it is negative 4)

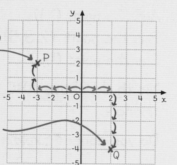

(x,y) – horizontal distance, vertical distance

CHECK-IN
JUSTAROO Airlines

1 Plot the point with coordinates (4,3)
2 Plot the point with coordinates (0,2)
3 Write down the coordinates of point A
4 Complete: The coordinates of point B are (__,__)

Ready for take off?

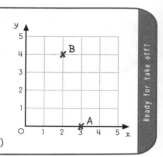

e.g. 2 Write down the coordinates of A, B and C

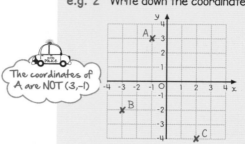

The coordinates of A are NOT (3,–1)

Point A is 1 left and 3 up
The point A is at (–1,3)

Point B is 3 left and 2 down
The point B is at (–3,–2)

Point C is 2 right and 4 down
The point C is at (2,–4)

We can solve problems in four quadrants:

e.g. 3 ABCD is a rectangle
A is the point (2,3)
B is the point (–3,3)
C is the point (–3,–1)
Find the coordinates of point D

1 Plot points A, B and C

2 Identify the rectangle (joining A to B and B to C will help)

3 Find the coordinates of point D

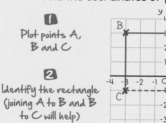

The coordinates of point D are (2,–1)

A. Plot and label the points.

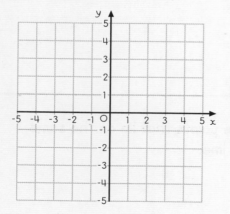

(i) W (–2,4)   (iii) Y (–2,–4)
(ii) X (2,–4)   (iv) Z (–4,0)

B. Here are five points on a grid.

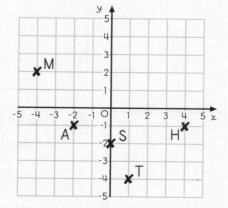

Write down the coordinates of point:

(i) M   (iii) T   (v) S
(ii) A   (iv) H

SET?

C. The points A, B and C are three corners of a rectangle.
Find the coordinates of the fourth corner.

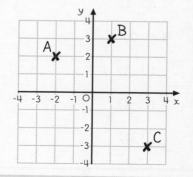

COORDINATES 2

1. Charlie is asked to plot the point A (−1,3).

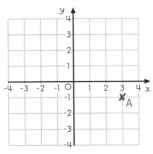

Do you agree? Explain your answer.

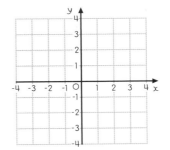

☐ (−4,3)

☐ (−2,1)

☐ (−4,−3)

☐ (3,−2)

☐ (−1,−3)

2. Tick the three points that join together to make a right-angled triangle.

3. The coordinates of A are (2,−4).

B is on the same vertical line as A.

Find possible coordinates for point B.

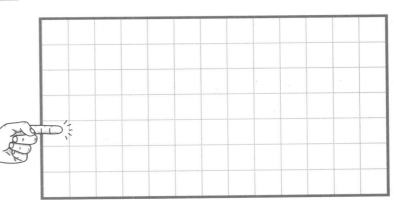

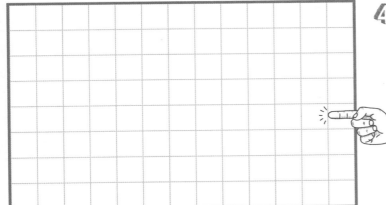

4. The points A (−3,−2) and B (−3,2) are two corners of a square.

Find a pair of coordinates for the other corners of the square.

READY?

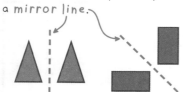

Reflections are one of the ways we can move and change shapes and letters.

A reflection 'flips' shapes and letters in a mirror line.

A reflected shape is the same distance from the mirror line as the original shape

e.g. 1 Reflect the shape in the mirror line.

1 Count from each corner to the mirror line and then count the same distance on the other side

Mirror line

2 Join the points to create the new shape

1 Find the coordinates of points A, B and C

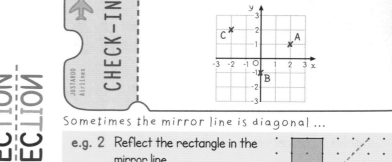

Sometimes the mirror line is diagonal ...

e.g. 2 Reflect the rectangle in the mirror line.

1 This time, count the diagonal distance to the mirror line

2 Create the image

Posh word for the reflected shape

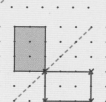

We can also reflect shapes on a coordinate grid ...

e.g. 3 The triangle is reflected in the x-axis. Write down the coordinates of the vertices of the new shape.

1 Reflect the shape

Mirror line

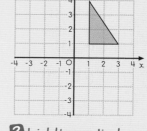

2 List the coordinates of the vertices (corners)

(1,–1)

(3,–1) and (1,–4)

SET?

A. Reflect each shape in the mirror line

(i)

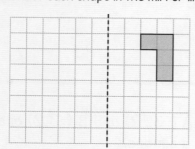

(iii)

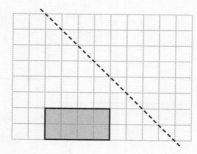

(ii)

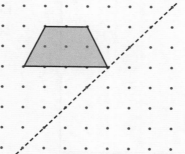

(iv)

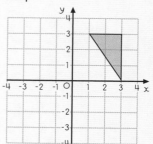

B. The triangle is reflected in the y-axis.

Write down the coordinates of the vertices of the new shape.

GO!

REFLECTIONS

1. The shape is reflected in both lines A and B. Complete the diagram.

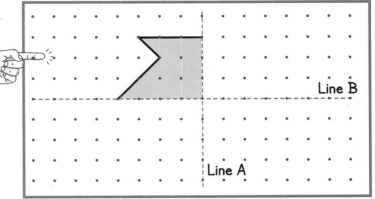

Line B

Line A

2. Fern is asked to reflect a shape. Here is her working:

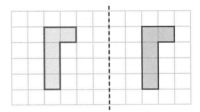

Fern is not correct. Explain why.

3. A triangle is reflected in the y-axis.

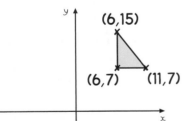

(6,15)

(6,7)   (11,7)

Find the coordinates of the vertices of the image.

4. A trapezium is reflected in different mirror lines.

Tick all the correct reflections.

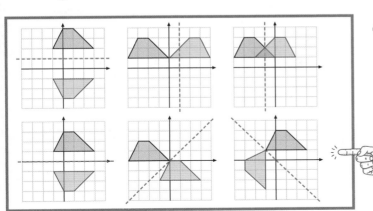

READY?

Translations are one of the ways we can move and change shapes and letters.

A *translation* 'slides' shapes and letters horizontally or vertically (or both).

TRANSLATION

TRANSLATION

TRANSLATION

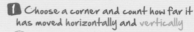
CHECK-IN JUSTAROO Airlines

1 Match each arrow to the direction it is pointing:

Left

Right

Up

Down

Ready for take off?

e.g. 1 Translate triangle A three squares to the right.

1 Choose a corner, move it 3 squares to the right

2 Repeat for all the other corners and join them up

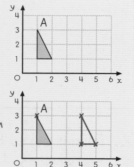

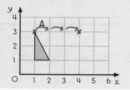

e.g. 2 Translate shape B four squares to the left and one square up.

1 Choose a corner, move it 4 squares to the left and 1 square up

2 Repeat for all the other corners and join them up

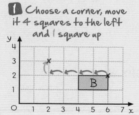

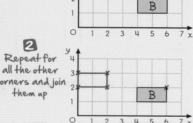

We can describe how shapes have been translated:

e.g. 3 Describe the translation that moves shape A to shape B.

1 Choose a corner and count how far it has moved horizontally and vertically

Start at A

Do NOT just find the distance between the shapes

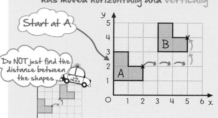

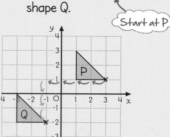

2 Check the other corners

3 squares right and 2 squares up

We can also work in all four quadrants ...

e.g. 4 Describe the translation that moves shape P to shape Q.

Start at P

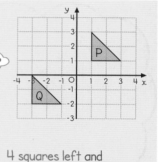

4 squares left and 3 squares down

A translation moves a shape horizontally or vertically (or both)

A. Translate shape A four squares to the left.

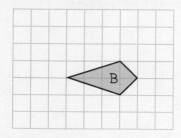

B. Translate shape B two squares up.

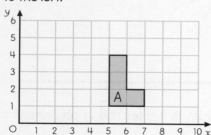

C. Translate shape C three squares to the right and one square down.

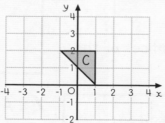

D. Describe the translation that moves shape D to shape E.

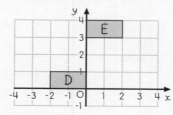

SET?

E. Describe the translation that moves shape P to shape Q.

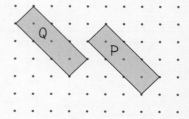

 **GO!**

TRANSLATIONS

1. The point (−2,4) is moved using the translation 5 squares right and 4 squares up, followed by the translation 3 squares left and 2 squares down.

Find the coordinates of the new point.

2. Sachin thinks he has translated shape A two squares right and one square up.

Sachin is not correct. Explain why.

3. Rectangle A has been translated.

(8,6)

(2,☐)

Find the missing numbers and words.

The translation is ☐ squares ☐

and 10 squares ☐

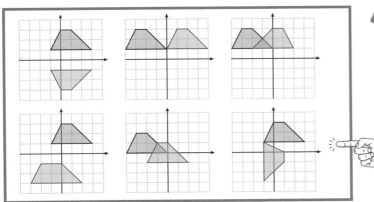

4. Tick the trapeziums that have been translated.

READY?

Tables are a useful way of organising and presenting information using rows and columns.

Rows left/right →
Columns up/down ↓

	Maths	English
Boys	6	10
Girls	8	12

e.g. 1 The table shows the number of pupils in a school.

	Class A	Class B
Boys	20	13
Girls	12	15

a) How many boys are in Class A?

b) How many more girls are in Class B than Class A?

c) How many pupils are in Class A altogether?

a) 20 ← The number of boys in Class A

b) 15 − 12 = 3

c) 20 + 12 = 32

	Class A	Class B
Boys	20	13
Girls	12	15

e.g. 2 The table show the prices of concert tickets for two bands.

	Mathmos	BABA
Adult	£25	£18
Child	£15	£12

a) How much is an adult ticket to see BABA? £18

b) How much does it cost two adults and one child to see Mathmos?

$$2 \times £25 + £15 = £65$$

What number is the arrow pointing at?

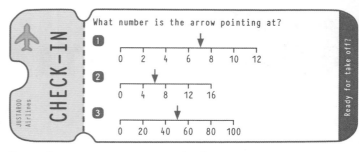

① 0 2 4 6 8 10 12

② 0 4 8 12 16

③ 0 20 40 60 80 100

Bar charts are a type of chart used to represent information. They can be vertical or horizontal. These two bar charts show the same information:

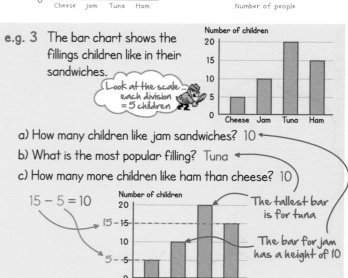

Number of people — Cheese, Jam, Tuna, Ham

Ham, Tuna, Jam, Cheese — Number of people

e.g. 3 The bar chart shows the fillings children like in their sandwiches.

Look at the scale... each division = 5 children

a) How many children like jam sandwiches? 10

b) What is the most popular filling? Tuna

c) How many more children like ham than cheese? 10

15 − 5 = 10

The tallest bar is for tuna

The bar for jam has a height of 10

A. The table shows the number of pupils in a school.

	Class A	Class B
Boys	18	13
Girls	13	12

(i) How many girls are in Class B?

(ii) How many more boys are in Class A than Class B?

B. The table shows the sponsor money collected by Sally and Frank.

	Walk	Silence
Sally	£8	£12.50
Frank	£10.50	£14

(i) How much money did Sally collect in total?

(ii) How much money did Frank collect by doing a walk?

(iii) How much more money did Frank collect for his silence than Sally?

C.

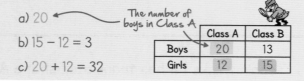

The bar chart shows the favourite type of music in a club.

(i) How many people like jazz?

(ii) What is the most popular type of music?

(iii) What is the difference between the number of people choosing pop and R&B?

(iv) How many people are in the club?

D. Use the bar chart to complete the table.

Tennis, Football, Rugby, Swimming — Total people

Sport	Total people
Tennis	
Football	
Rugby	
Swimming	

1. Here are the ticket prices at a cinema:

	Adult	Child
Monday to Friday	£7.50	£5
Saturday	£10	£7.50
Sunday	£5	£5

How much does it cost Tessa to take her two children to the cinema on a Tuesday?

2. The bar chart shows the amount of money Freddy spent in a week.

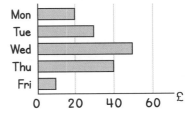

Tick the correct statements.

The largest amount of money Freddy spent is £45

Freddy spent £20 more on Thursday than Friday

Freddy spent £30 on Tuesday

Freddy spent £5 less on Friday than Monday

Freddy spent a total of £150

3. 60 children were asked, "What is your favourite pet?"

15 children chose rat.
10 more children chose cat than rat.
The same number of children chose dog as chose fish.

Complete the bar chart.

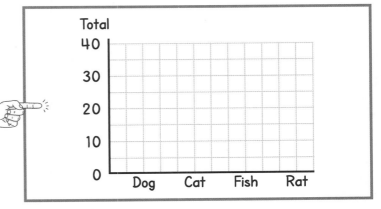

4. Some pupils are asked how they travel to school.

Tick all the bar charts that represent the same information.

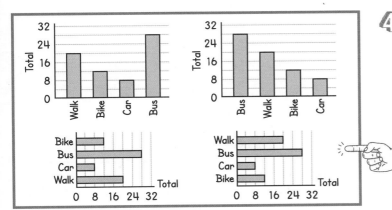

READY?

Line graphs show the pattern (also called 'trend') of data over a period of time:

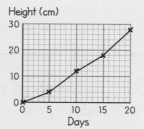

Each point on a line graph (×) shows a value at a particular moment in time. Points are joined to each other using straight lines.

e.g. 1 The line graph shows the height of a sunflower.

What was the height of the sunflower after 10 days?

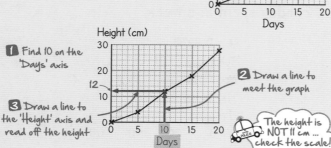

1 Find 10 on the 'Days' axis

2 Draw a line to meet the graph

3 Draw a line to the 'Height' axis and read off the height

The height is NOT 11 cm ... check the scale!

The height of the sunflower is 12 cm

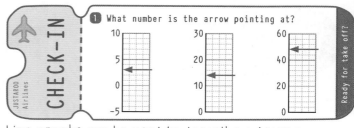
Line graphs can be used to describe a journey ...

e.g. 2 Matt goes on a bike ride from his house. The line graph shows his journey.

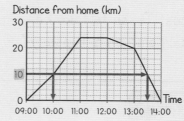

a) At what times was Matt 10 km from his house?

b) What do you think happened between 11:00 and 12:00?

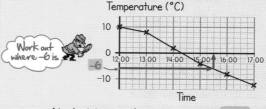

a) 10:00 and 13:30

b) The graph is flat so the distance hasn't changed. Matt could have stopped for a rest.

Line graphs can show positive and negative values:

e.g. 3 The line graph shows the temperature during a day.

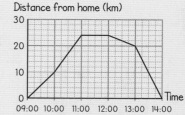

Work out where −6 is

At what time is the temperature −6°C? 15:30

A. The line graph shows the height of a plant.

Find the height of the plant after:

(i) 5 days

(ii) 10 days

(iii) 17 days

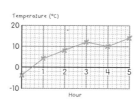

Height (mm)

B. The line graph shows the temperature during a day.

(i) Find the temperature at 13:00

(ii) Find the temperature at 11:30

(iii) When was the temperature 13°C?

(iv) Between what times is the temperature the same?

C. The line graph shows a car journey.

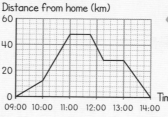

SET?

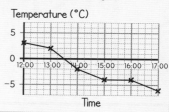

(i) How far is the car from home at 10:00?

(ii) For how long does the car stop when 28 km from home?

D. The line graph shows the temperature during an experiment.

(i) At what time is the temperature 0°C?

(ii) What was the temperature at 14:00?

158

GO!

LINE GRAPHS

1. Use different digits to complete the statement about this line graph:

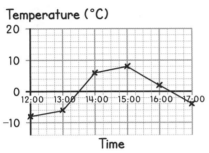

Temperature (°C)

Time

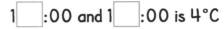

The difference in temperature between

1☐:00 and 1☐:00 is 4°C

The difference in temperature between

1☐:00 and 1☐:30 is 11°C

2. The line graph shows information about Megan's run.

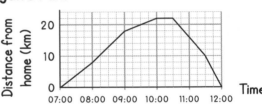

Distance from home (km)

Time

07:00 08:00 09:00 10:00 11:00 12:00

She says, "At 07:30 I was 2 km from home"

Do you agree? Explain why.

3. Here is a line graph.

a) Use the information below to add times and depths to the axes.

Two taps are turned on	One tap is turned off when the depth is 18 cm
At 6 p.m. one tap is turned off	The plug was first pulled out at 7:30 p.m.

b) At what times is the sink empty of water?

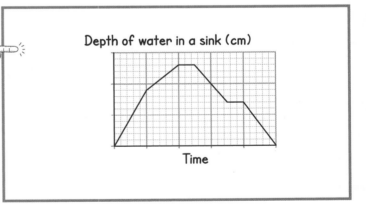

Depth of water in a sink (cm)

Time

4. The line graph shows the temperature in a city across a year.

What is the difference in temperature between the coldest and warmest months?

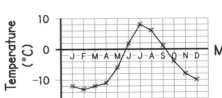

Temperature (°C)

J F M A M J J A S O N D

Month

READY?

A pie chart can be used to represent data.

Here are some pie charts that show children's favourite sports for three different classes:

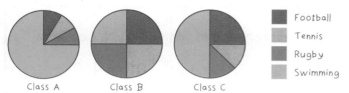

Class A   Class B   Class C

Football
Tennis
Rugby
Swimming

Each section of the pie chart shows the proportion of the class that like each sport.

e.g. 1a A class were asked to name their favourite animal. The pie chart shows the results.

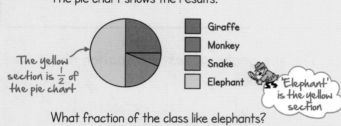

Giraffe
Monkey
Snake
Elephant

The yellow section is $\frac{1}{2}$ of the pie chart

'Elephant' is the yellow section

What fraction of the class like elephants?

$\frac{1}{2}$ of the class like elephants

Percentages can also be used to describe pie charts ...

e.g. 1b What percentage of the class like giraffes?

'Giraffe' is the blue section

The blue section is $\frac{1}{4}$ of the pie chart (25%)

25% of the class like giraffes

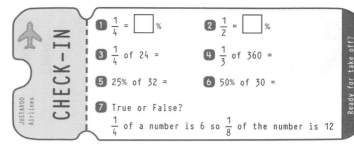

CHECK-IN   JUSTAROO Airlines   Ready for take off?

1 $\frac{1}{4}$ = ☐ %   2 $\frac{1}{2}$ = ☐ %

3 $\frac{1}{4}$ of 24 =   4 $\frac{1}{3}$ of 360 =

5 25% of 32 =   6 50% of 30 =

7 True or False?
$\frac{1}{4}$ of a number is 6 so $\frac{1}{8}$ of the number is 12

Pie charts can also be used to work out the number represented by each section ...

e.g. 2 The pie chart shows the number of goals scored by a team in 12 matches.

0
1
2
3

'2 goals' is the white section

In how many games did the team score 2 goals?

The white section is $\frac{1}{4}$ of the pie chart → $\frac{1}{4}$ of 12 = 3

2 goals were scored in 3 matches

e.g. 3 The pie chart shows information about 24 people. Use the pie chart to complete the table:

Football
Rugby
Tennis
Swimming

Sport	Number of people
Football	
Rugby	
Tennis	
Swimming	

Top tip ... look for 'nice' fractions to get started: e.g. both pink and green sections are $\frac{1}{4}$

Sport	Number of people
Football	9
Rugby	3
Tennis	6
Swimming	6

3 This section is left till last ...
24 – (6 + 6 + 3) = 9

2 This section is half of one quarter ...
6 ÷ 2 = 3

1 $\frac{1}{4}$ of 24 = 6

A. A class were asked to name their favourite day of the week. The pie chart shows the results.

Friday
Saturday
Sunday
Monday

(i) What fraction of the class chose Friday?

(ii) What percentage of the class chose Saturday?

B. 32 children were asked to name their favourite pet.

The pie chart shows the results.

Tick the correct statements:

Rabbit
Cat   Fish
Dog

☐ 16 children chose rabbit
☐ 50% of children chose dog
☐ The same number of children chose cat as fish
☐ 4 children chose cat
☐ One third of the children chose fish
☐ Twice as many children chose dog than rabbit

C. The pie chart above shows the results of asking 24 teachers to name their favourite drink.

Tea
Coffee
Water

SET?

(i) How many teachers chose tea?

(ii) How many teachers chose coffee?

D. Use the pie chart to complete the table:

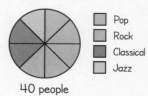

Pop
Rock
Classical
Jazz

40 people

Music	Number of people
Pop	
Rock	
Classical	
Jazz	

1. Here is a pie chart showing the favourite food for 16 children:

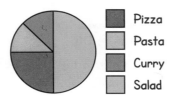

- Pizza
- Pasta
- Curry
- Salad

Use the information to complete the bar chart.

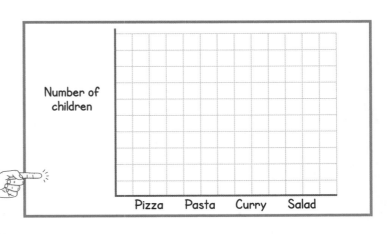

Number of children

Pizza   Pasta   Curry   Salad

Subject	Number of people
Maths	
English	6
History	
Science	

2. Use the information to find all the missing numbers.

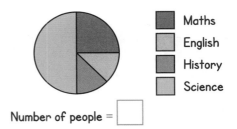

- Maths
- English
- History
- Science

Number of people = ☐

3. There are 32 pupils in a class. The pie chart shows the number of pets each pupil has:

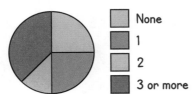

- None
- 1
- 2
- 3 or more

Ty says, "25 pupils have no pet".

Ty is not correct. Explain why.

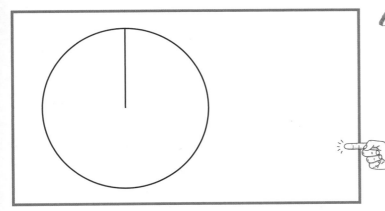

4. Here is some information about how Saira spends her money:

- * 25% is spent on clothes
- * $\frac{1}{3}$ is spent on petrol
- * The rest of her money is spent on food

Sketch a pie chart to show this information.

READY?

Mel, Steve, Chris and Matt have some cookies:

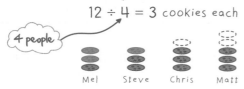

Mel   Steve   Chris   Matt

The information about the cookies can be listed as a set of data, in this case: 1, 2, 4, 5

Averages are a way of analysing data by trying to find the central, or typical, value. One type of average is called the mean ...

* Altogether, Mel, Steve, Chris and Matt have:

$$1 + 2 + 4 + 5 = 12 \text{ cookies}$$

* Let's share them equally:

$$12 \div 4 = 3 \text{ cookies each}$$

4 people

Mel   Steve   Chris   Matt

The mean number of cookies is 3

e.g. 1   Calculate the mean of 2, 3, 1 and 6

1   There are four numbers

Find the sum of the numbers:

Sum of the numbers = $2 + 3 + 1 + 6 = 12$

2

Divide the sum by the number of items in the set of data:

Mean = $12 \div 4 = 3$

CHECK-IN   JUSTAROO Airlines   Ready for take off?

1 Calculate:

$21 \div 3 =$ $4 + 4 + 4 + 1.5 + 1.5 =$

2 Circle the correct answer to $13 \div 2$

   6.1   6.2   6.3   6.4   6.5

3 Circle the correct answer to $10 \div 4$

   2.2   2.3   2.4   2.5

e.g. 2   Find the mean of 1, 3, 6, 5 and 5

1 Sum = $1 + 3 + 6 + 5 + 5 = 20$

There are five numbers ...

2 Mean = $20 \div 5 = 4$

Do NOT divide before finding the sum

Sometimes the mean is not a whole number ...

e.g. 3   Find the mean of 0, 7, 9 and 6

1 Sum of the numbers = $0 + 7 + 9 + 6 = 22$

There are four numbers ...

2 Mean = $22 \div 4 = 5.5$

Remember ... dividing by 4 is the same as dividing by 2 and then dividing by 2 again

We can use the mean to solve problems ...

e.g. 4   Debbie has scored goals in her last 3 football matches.

In two of the matches, she scored 2 goals.
In her other match, she scored 5 goals.

What is the mean number of goals Debbie scored?

Debbie has scored 2, 2 and 5 goals

1 Sum of the numbers = $2 + 2 + 5 = 9$

There are three numbers ...

2 Mean = $9 \div 3 = 3$

Mean number of goals = 3

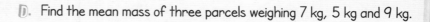

A. Find the mean of each set of data:

(i) 2, 2, 3, 1

(ii) 1, 4, 6, 4, 5

(iii) 1, 0, 2, 5, 2

B. Find the mean of each set of data:

(i) 5, 6, 4

(ii) 2, 8, 4, 6

(iii) 0, 1, 0, 4, 5

C. Find the mean of each set of data:

(i) 3, 2, 1, 4

(ii) 4, 5, 3, 8

(iii) 0, 1, 2, 3

D. Find the mean mass of three parcels weighing 7 kg, 5 kg and 9 kg.

E. Tomas walks to school taking different routes each day.

Three of the days he walks 4 km each day.
On each of the other two days he walks 1.5 km.

What was the mean number of kilometres Tomas walked?

1. The mean of four different numbers is 5
   Two of the numbers are 2 and 8
   The other two numbers are even.
   Find the missing numbers.

2 [ ] [ ] 8

2. Tobias is asked to calculate the mean of

   2   0   4   6   8

   He writes:
   2 + 4 + 6 + 8 = 20
   20 ÷ 4 = 5
   Mean = 5

   Explain why Tobias is not correct.

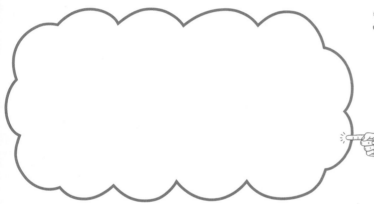

3. The table shows the amount of rainfall over five days:

Day	Mon	Tue	Wed	Thu	Fri
Rainfall (mm)	5	4.5	1.6	2.5	1.4

   Work out the mean amount of rainfall.

4. The mean test score for 6 pupils is 12
   Another pupil takes the test and scores 5
   Find the mean test score for the 7 pupils.

HINT: Find the total score for the 6 pupils first

A ratio describes how the size of one quantity compares to the size of another quantity ...

* in a class of 12 pupils, the number of girls is twice the number of boys:

* in a packet of 15 sweets, the number of orange sweets is four times the number of blue sweets:

e.g. 1 A necklace is made using 4 blue beads for every 1 pink bead. The necklace has 20 beads.
How many blue and pink beads does it have?

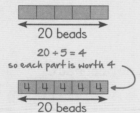

5 beads
10 beads
15 beads
20 beads

Keep repeating the pattern

16 blue beads and 4 pink beads

OR

The pattern repeats every 5 beads, and there are 20 beads in total

20 beads

$20 ÷ 5 = 4$
so each part is worth 4

4 4 4 4 4

20 beads

Blue: $4 × 4 = 16$ beads
Pink: $1 × 4 = 4$ beads

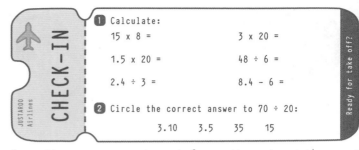

JUSTAROO Airlines

CHECK-IN

❶ Calculate:
$15 × 8 =$ $3 × 20 =$

$1.5 × 20 =$ $48 ÷ 6 =$

$2.4 ÷ 3 =$ $8.4 - 6 =$

❷ Circle the correct answer to $70 ÷ 20$:

3.10   3.5   35   15

Ready for take off?

Sometimes we are given information about the part and not the whole ...

e.g. 2 Every pupil is given 3 pencils and 2 rubbers.
15 pencils are given out. How many rubbers are needed?

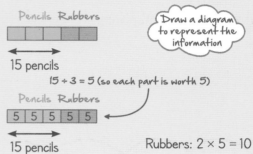

Pencils   Rubbers

15 pencils

Draw a diagram to represent the information

$15 ÷ 3 = 5$ (so each part is worth 5)

Pencils   Rubbers
5 5 5 5 5

15 pencils

Rubbers: $2 × 5 = 10$

Maps and scale drawings also use ratio ...

e.g. 3 On a map, 1 cm represents 10 km.
A road measures 4 cm on the map.
How long is the actual road?

Putting the information in a ratio table can help

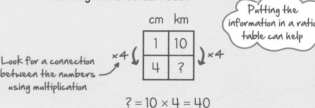

cm   km

×4 | 1 | 10 | ×4
     | 4 | ? |

Look for a connection between the numbers using multiplication

$? = 10 × 4 = 40$
The road is 40 km long

Ⓐ. A necklace is made using 5 red beads for every 1 yellow bead. Complete the table:

Number of red beads	Number of yellow beads	Total number of beads
		18
		30
		48
		60

Ⓑ. Every pupil in a class is given 5 pencils and 2 pens.
How many pens are needed if 100 pencils are given out?

Ⓒ. Beryl bakes some scones.
For every 7 scones, only 2 scones have raisins.
She bakes 10 scones that have raisins.
How many scones did Beryl bake?

Ⓓ. On a map, 1 cm represents 20 km. Complete the table:

Map distance	Real-life distance
3 cm	
	100 km
1.5 cm	
	70 km

1. A drink is made using water and lemon squash.

Nine times as much water is needed than lemon squash.

Mo makes 2 litres of the drink. How much lemon squash does she need?

[_____ ml]

2. A necklace is made using 5 red beads for every 2 yellow beads. There are 20 red beads in total.

Sharon thinks there will be 2 + 15 = 17 yellow beads.

Explain why Sharon is not correct.

3. Eight burgers cost £12

Four burgers and three packets of fries costs £8.40

How much does one packet of fries cost?

[£]

4. The London Eye is a large ferris wheel in London.

Ally makes a scale model of the London Eye using the scale 1 cm to 15 m.

The height of her scale model is 9 cm.

What is the height of the London Eye?

5. Complete the description of a necklace using the digits 1, 2, 3, 4 and 5

A necklace has [ ] red beads for every [ ] blue bead.

It has [ ][ ] red beads and 1 [ ] blue beads.

 # READY?

Missing number problems, for example

$$\square + 6 = 15$$

can also be written using algebraic notation (using letters), such as

$$n + 6 = 15$$

where n represents an unknown (number). Algebraic notation that we need to be happy with includes:

Algebra says ...	We say ...
$n + 2$	n add 2
$n - 2$	n subtract 2
$2 - n$	2 subtract n
$2n$	2 multiplied by n
$\frac{n}{2}$	n divided by 2
n^2	n squared*

*or n times itself

e.g. 1 $n + 3 = 8$
Find the value of n.

Read $n + 3 = 8$ as an unknown (n) add 3 equals 8

 A bar model can be really helpful

8	
n	3

5
n

The inverse of addition is subtraction ... so subtract 3 from both bars to find the missing number

$$n = 5$$

e.g. 2 Solve $a - 5 = 8$

'Solve' means ... find the answer to the problem

Read $a - 5 = 8$ as an unknown (a) subtract 5 equals 8

The inverse of subtraction is addition

$$a = 8 + 5$$
$$a = 13$$

Missing number problems can also involve division or multiplication ...

e.g. 3 $2p = 24$
Find the value of p.

Read $2p = 24$ as an unknown (p) multiplied by 2 equals 24

The inverse operation of multiplication is division

$$p = 24 \div 2$$
$$p = 12$$

Missing number problems can also involve a pair of unknowns ...

e.g. 4 $x + y = 5$

x and y are positive whole numbers.

Complete the table with possible values for x and y.

x	y
4	1
3	2
2	3
1	4

Think about this as ... 'if the whole is 5, what could the value of the parts, x and y, be?'

A. Find the value of n:

(i) $n + 3 = 7$

(ii) $n + 6 = 14$

(iii) $n + 12 = 11$

B. Solve:

(i) $a - 7 = 11$

(ii) $b - 3 = 9$

(iii) $x - 12 = 20$

C. Solve:

(i) $2a = 16$

(ii) $2p = 20$

(iii) $3x = 18$

D. Solve:

(i) $\frac{n}{2} = 10$

(ii) $\frac{b}{5} = 3$

 SET?

E. $a + b = 7$

a and b are positive whole numbers. Complete the table with possible values for a and b.

a	b

HINT: The inverse operation of division is multiplication

166

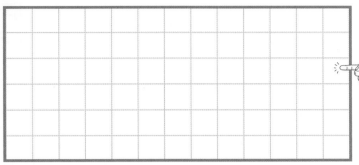

INTRODUCTION TO ALGEBRA

1. Sonny thinks of two numbers.

The sum of the two numbers is 11

The product of the two numbers is 24

Find the two numbers.

2. Dev is solving 2x = 28

He writes:

$$x = 8$$

Do you agree? Explain your answer.

3. Find the values of △ and ○

Total 28

Total 25

△ =

○ =

4. Find the value of a

12		a	5
6	a	7	a

5. a + b = 12

ab = 32

a > b

Find the values of a and b.

READY?

A formula is a rule (in words or letters) showing the relationship between different quantities. Substituting into a formula means replacing these words or letters with numbers.

We can use formulae (the plural of formula) such as:

Perimeter (P) of a square = 4 × length of one side

Distance travelled by a car on a journey = average speed × time taken

Cost in pounds of hiring a car = number of days hired × 20 then + 7

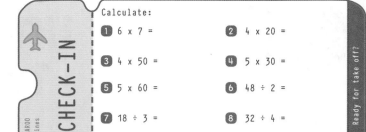

JUSTAROO Airlines

CHECK-IN

Ready for take off?

Calculate:

1. 6 × 7 =
2. 4 × 20 =
3. 4 × 50 =
4. 5 × 30 =
5. 5 × 60 =
6. 48 ÷ 2 =
7. 18 ÷ 3 =
8. 32 ÷ 4 =
9. 280 ÷ 4 =
10. 280 ÷ 40 =

e.g. 1 The perimeter (P) of a square can be calculated using the formula:

Perimeter (P) = 4 × length of one side

Use the formula to find the perimeter of a square with a side of length 3 cm.

P = 4 × 3 = 12 cm

Substitute the value (length = 3)

We can also use formulae with two quantities:

e.g. 2 This rule can be used to work out the distance travelled:

Distance travelled = average speed × time taken

Work out the distance travelled by a car travelling at an average speed of 50 mph for 4 hours.

Distance travelled = 50 × 4 = 200 miles

Substitute the values (speed = 50 and time = 4)

We can solve problems using formulae with more than one step ...

e.g. 3 The formula to work out the cost, in pounds, of hiring a car is:

Cost = number of days hired × 20 then + 7

Find the cost of hiring a car for 4 days.

Cost = 4 × 20 + 7
= 80 + 7
= £87

The cost is NOT 4 × 27 = £108 (4 × 20 first)

e.g. 4 Billie is buying bottles of juice for a children's party. She uses a formula:

Number of bottles = number of children ÷ 4 + 6

There will be 28 children at the party.
Work out the number of bottles of juice Billie needs.

Number of bottles = 28 ÷ 4 + 6
= 7 + 6
= 13

Substitute the value (number of children = 28)

SET?

A. Marty can work out how much money he earns in pounds using a formula:

Money earned = hours worked × 8

Marty works 7 hours.
How much does he earn?

B. The area of a rectangle can be calculated using the formula:

Area = length × width

Use the formula to find the area of a rectangle with length 9 cm and width 6 cm.

C. Here is a rule for working out the area of a triangle:

Multiply the length of the base by the perpendicular height.
Divide by 2

Use the rule to work out the area of a triangle with a base of 8 cm and a perpendicular height of 6 cm.

D. The rule for working out the cost (in pounds) of hiring a bike is:

Multiply the number of days hired by 7 and then add 15

Find the cost of hiring a bike for five days.

E. Stanley is buying cakes for a party.

He uses a formula:

Number of cakes = number of people ÷ 3 + 2

There will be 18 people at the party.

Work out the number of cakes Stanley needs.

NOTE: Units for B and C are cm²

GO!

1. Kitty uses uses this formula to work out the cooking time for some meat in minutes:

> Time = weight of meat in kg × 30 then + 20

Kitty starts to cook the meat at 12:15 p.m.

The weight of the meat is 3 kg.

At what time is the meat cooked?

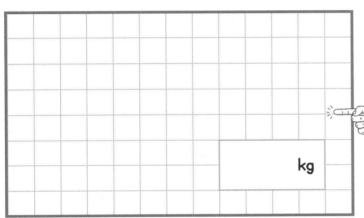

kg

2. The time (T) needed to cook a chicken can be calculated using the rule:

> allow 20 minutes plus 40 minutes per kilogram

Calculate the mass of a chicken if it takes five hours to cook.

3. A formula for the cost of hiring a hot tub is:

Cost (£) = 40 + number of days hired × 50

Ed hires a hot tub for 2 days.

Beyonce hires a hot tub for 4 days.

Beyonce says:

"It will cost me twice as much as Ed".

Beyonce is wrong. Explain why.

4. Here is a pattern of number pairs:

a	b
1	8
2	18
3	28
4	38

Complete the rule that connects the number pairs.

$$b = \boxed{} \times a - \boxed{}$$

Drawing a picture is a useful strategy to help solve word problems. The **bar model** is a powerful diagram that we can use. It is useful to look for **key words** in the problem to help decide which type of bar model to draw:

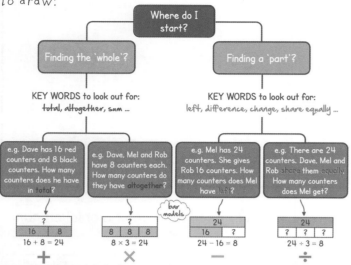

Where do I start?

Finding the 'whole'?

KEY WORDS to look out for:
total, altogether, sum ...

e.g. Dave has 16 red counters and 8 black counters. How many counters does he have in total?

```
|  ?  |
| 16 | 8 |
16 + 8 = 24
```
+

e.g. Dave, Mel and Rob have 8 counters each. How many counters do they have altogether?

```
|   ?   |
| 8 | 8 | 8 |
8 × 3 = 24
```
×

Finding a 'part'?

KEY WORDS to look out for:
left, difference, change, share equally ...

e.g. Mel has 24 counters. She gives Rob 16 counters. How many counters does Mel have left?

```
|   24   |
| 16 | ? |
24 − 16 = 8
```
−

e.g. There are 24 counters. Dave, Mel and Rob share them equally. How many counters does Mel get?

```
|    24    |
| ? | ? | ? |
24 ÷ 3 = 8
```
÷

bar models

e.g. 1 Mia, Nia and Oona have collected merits during a school term.

How many merits have they collected in total?

Name	Merits
Mia	398
Nia	276
Oona	419

1 Draw a diagram to represent the information:

Total?		
398	276	419

2 Use addition to find the total: 398 + 276 + 419 = 1,093 merits

e.g. 2 Beth makes bracelets using beads.

Each bracelet uses 12 beads.

Beth makes 5 bracelets.

How many beads does Beth use altogether?

1 Diagram:

Altogether?				
12	12	12	12	12

2 Use multiplication to find the number of beads: 12 × 5 = 60 beads

Sometimes we are given the whole ...

e.g. 3 John buys a coffee for £2.75 and a cake for £1.20

He pays with a £10 note.

How much money does he have left?

2.75 + 1.20 = 3.95

1 Diagram:

10		
2.75	1.20	Left?

2 What does John spend?

10	
3.95	Left?

3 Use subtraction to find the solution: £10 − £3.95 = £6.05 left

Sometimes we need to find equal parts ...

e.g. 4 Mel is creating a book.

Each book needs 80 sheets of paper.

Mel has 720 sheets of paper.

How many complete books can Mel make?

The paper is shared equally

1 Diagram:

720		
80	80	... how many 80s do we need?

2 Use division to find the number of books: 720 ÷ 80 = 9 books

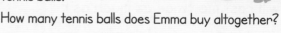

A bar model is a sketch that represents the information (not a scale diagram!)

A. Billie is playing a computer game.

She scores 256 points on Level 1, 417 points on Level 2 and 534 points on Level 3

What is Billie's total score?

B. Tom has £20

He spends £4.60 on drinks and £8.15 on food.

How much money does Tom have left?

C. There are 60 cards in a board game.

Ari, Barry, Carrie and Doug share the cards equally.

How many cards does Carrie get?

D. Tennis balls are sold in packs of five.

Emma buys eight packs of tennis balls.

How many tennis balls does Emma buy altogether?

E. A large box contains 25 sweets.

Dave buys 5 large boxes of sweets.

How many sweets does Dave buy altogether?

F. 360 pupils go on a school trip. They travel by coach.

50 pupils can travel on each coach.

How many coaches are needed to transport all the pupils?

SET?

GO!

SOLVING WORD PROBLEMS

1. Dominic reads $\frac{1}{3}$ of a book.

He has read 240 pages.

How many pages are left for Dominic to read?

2. A box of crisps holds 28 packets.
A box of nuts holds 14 packets.

Tim buys 8 boxes of nuts. Sheila buys 4 boxes of crisps.

Tim says,

"I have more packets than Sheila in total".

Explain why Tim is not correct.

3. Jason makes bracelets and necklaces.

12 beads are used to make a bracelet.
45 beads are used to make a necklace.

Jason makes 7 bracelets and 3 necklaces.

How many beads does Jason use in total?

4. There are 4,200 leaflets in a box.

Ally and Bea take 700 leaflets each.

Charlie and Dave share the rest of the leaflets equally.

How many leaflets does Dave have?

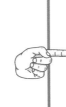

5. Four pineapples cost the same as six melons.

A pineapple costs £1.20

How much does one melon cost?

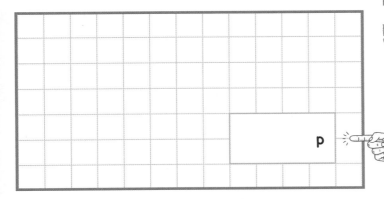

P

Extra space for workings

173

Extra space for workings

Solutions this way

(But only if you have done the question first)

... also available online

Place Value 1 (p.10)

Check-in

1	Three hundred and fourteen
2	230
3	Ring around: 400

Set?

A	(i) 8 ten thousands or 80,000 or eighty thousand (ii) 8 hundreds or 800 or eight hundred (iii) 8 thousands or 8,000 or eight thousand (iv) 8 hundred thousands or 800,000 or eight hundred thousand
B	(i) 67,423 (ii) 6,062 (iii) 800,080
C	(i) Fifty-four thousand, four hundred and seventeen (ii) Sixty-two thousand and ninety-one (iii) One hundred and forty thousand, three hundred and seven
D	41,709
E	292,200

Go!

1

1,000 less	Number	1,000 more
37,734	38,734	39,734
309,627	310,627	311,627
9,070	10,070	11,070

2	He has used incorrect place value. The correct answer is 136,070
3	12,000
4	40,025 40,205 42,005
5	A approximately 90,000 B approximately 150,000 C approximately 310,000

Place Value 2 (p.12)

Check-in

1	Forty thousand, five hundred and twenty-six
2	310,578
3	Ring around: 20,000

Set?

A	(i) 6 millions or 6,000,000 or six million (ii) 6 hundred thousands or 600,000 or six hundred thousand (iii) 6 ten thousands or 60,000 or sixty thousand
B	(i) 5,000,000 (ii) 5,357,261 (iii) 5,053,000
C	(i) One million, two hundred and forty-six thousand, seven hundred and eighty-three (ii) Three million, seven hundred and twenty-six thousand and seventy (iii) Four hundred and one thousand, eight hundred and ninety-six (iv) Ten million
D	6,237,601
E	5,123,500

Go!

1	Nine hundred and ninety-nine thousand, nine hundred and ninety-nine
2	No, she has missed the hundreds digit. The correct answer should be 6,600,066

3

1,900,000	Nine million
90,000	One million nine hundred thousand
900,000	Nine hundred thousand
19,000	One hundred and ninety thousand
9,000,000	Nineteen thousand
190,000	Ninety thousand

4	850,000
5	A approximately 800,000 B approximately 1,500,000 C approximately 2,200,000

Comparing and Ordering 1 (p.14)

Check-in

1	7 25 27 37 73
2	greater less

Set?

A	(i) < (ii) > (iii) < (iv) > (v) <
B	(i) > (ii) > (iii) > (iv) >
C	Ring around: (i) 456 (ii) 132 (iii) 98 (iv) 204 (v) 784
D	(i) 278 478 724 872 (ii) 54 540 543 547 (iii) 99 807 909 990

Go!

1	A possible solution: (largest to smallest) 987, 978, 798, 789
2	No. 314 is the largest number because it has the largest hundreds digit
3	Sometimes true. For example, 900 is greater than 120 but 790 is smaller than 800

4

678	1st
87	2nd
687	3rd
786	4th
768	5th

5	280 281 285 291

Comparing and Ordering 2 (p.16)

Check-in

1	81 180 801 810 880
2	less greater

Set?

A	(i) < (ii) > (iii) < (iv) < (v) >
B	(i) > (ii) < (iii) > (iv) >
C	Ring around: (i) 65,432 (ii) 635,823 (iii) 95,802
D	(i) 25,263 35,432 52,536 53,237 (ii) 76,897 145,802 242,237 351,654 (iii) 30,500 30,503 30,530 35,000 (iv) 9,256 9,265 10,072 10,702

Go!

1	A possible solution: 12,654 < 20,456 53, 807 > 52,708 4,312 < 59,213
2	No. The height for K2 is larger than the height for K12
3	Boxes ticked: 450,000 910,500 Half a million
4	A possible solution: 132,716 132,781 132,853 142,857

Comparing and Ordering 3 (p.18)

Check-in

1	Ring around: 201,000	
2	>	<

Set?

A	(i) < (ii) > (iii) < (iv) < (v) <
B	(i) < (ii) > (iii) < (iv) =

C	Ring around:
	(i) 3,350,798
	(ii) 9,521,654
	(iii) 2,400,002
	(iv) 4 million

D				
(i)	2,345,263	3,456,432	3,876,237	4,765,536
(ii)	2,127,823	2,516,987	3,106,798	4,615,897
(iii)	230,500	2,003,530	2,030,503	2,300,050

Go!

1	Possible solutions:
	3,665,500 > 3,480,500
	3,664,500 > 3,580,500
	3,566,500 > 3,480,500
2	She has not compared the millions column. The largest number is 5,746,012
3	No. Donny is wrong, only Switzerland, Denmark and Bulgaria have a population greater than five million
4	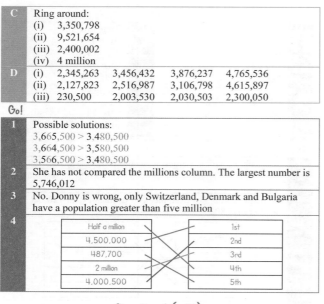

Half a million — 1st
4,500,000 — 2nd
487,700 — 3rd
2 million — 4th
4,000,500 — 5th

Rounding 1 (p.20)

Check-in

1	Rings around: 40 and 120
2	Rings around: 100 and 1,000
3	a) 45 b) 650

Set?

A		C	
(i)	50	(i)	200
(ii)	90	(ii)	500
(iii)	170	(iii)	200
(iv)	400	(iv)	800
(v)	800	(v)	1,000
B		D	
(i)	140	(i)	300
(ii)	560	(ii)	500
(iii)	710	(iii)	900
(iv)	300	(iv)	1,000

E	Statements ticked:
	435 rounded to the nearest 100
	350 rounded to the nearest 100
	405 rounded to the nearest 100
	404 rounded to the nearest 10

Go!

1	a) 450
	b) 495
2	e.g. He has rounded down when he should round up. The correct answer is 370
3	They could be both be correct if the number of sweets is between 595 and 604 as any of these will round to 600 to the nearest 10 and 600 to the nearest 100
4	597 rounded to the nearest 10 is 600 or 695 rounded to the nearest 10 is 700

Rounding 2 (p.22)

Check-in

1	Rings around: 20,000 100,000 150,000
2	7,500
3	Ring around: 200

Set?

A		C	
(i)	3,000	(i)	10,000
(ii)	7,000	(ii)	30,000
(iii)	8,000	(iii)	50,000
(iv)	1,000	(iv)	80,000
(v)	10,000	(v)	100,000
B		D	
(i)	13,000	(i)	30,000
(ii)	27,000	(ii)	40,000
(iii)	48,000	(iii)	50,000
(iv)	100,000	(iv)	30,000

E

15,675 to the nearest 1,000 — 15,680
15,675 to the nearest 10 — 22,000
18,500 to the nearest 10,000 — 19,000
20,950 to the nearest 100 — 16,000
21,500 to the nearest 1,000 — 21,000
15,675 to the nearest 100 — 20,000
18,500 to the nearest 1,000 — 15,700

Go!

1	a) 49,950
	b) 49,500
	c) 45,000
2	She has rounded to the nearest 1,000 not the nearest 10,000 The correct answer is 40,000
3	Yes because Justown population could be from 62,500 to 63,499 and Kanity population could be from 55,000 to 64,999
4	Sometimes true, e.g. 8,500 would round to 9,000 (4 digits) and 9,500 would round to 10,000 (5 digits) when rounding to the nearest 1,000

Rounding 3 (p.24)

Check-in

1	850,000
2	Ring around: B 13,000
3	Ring around: B 60,000

Set?

A	
(i)	130,000
(ii)	270,000
(iii)	380,000
(iv)	510,000
(v)	490,000
B	
(i)	140,000
(ii)	260,000
(iii)	370,000
(iv)	500,000
(v)	500,000
C	
(i)	100,000
(ii)	300,000
(iii)	300,000
(iv)	600,000
(v)	900,000
(vi)	100,000
D	
(i)	200,000
(ii)	200,000
(iii)	400,000
(iv)	600,000
(v)	1,000,000

Go!

1	Statements ticked:
	475,000 to the nearest 100,000
	501,501 to the nearest 100,000
2	She has rounded down. The correct answer is 300,000
3	A = 149,000
	B = 154,000
	C = 157,000
4	£104,999.99

Rounding 4 (p.26)

Check-in

1	1.04 1.3 1.35 1.4 1.42
2	7.5
3	6.35

Set?

A	
(i)	6
(ii)	3
(iii)	9
(iv)	4
(v)	13
B	
(i)	7
(ii)	17
(iii)	9
(iv)	43
(v)	13
C	
(i)	6.5
(ii)	16.6
(iii)	9.4
(iv)	43.1
(v)	0.8
(vi)	0.1
D	
(i)	6.2
(ii)	16.8
(iii)	0.4
(iv)	43.6
(v)	0.8

Go!

1	She has rounded each cost to the nearest £1 £2 + £1 + £3 + £3 + £1 = £10
2	She has rounded down. The correct answer is 1
3	11.5 (seconds)
4	Any four from: 5.78 to the nearest whole number is 6 5.87 to the nearest whole number is 6 7.56 to the nearest whole number is 8 7.65 to the nearest whole number is 8 6.58 to the nearest whole number is 7 6.85 to the nearest whole number is 7

Counting and Sequences (p.28)

Check-in

1	72		68
	90		50
	79		61
	81		63
	920		520

Set?

A	0 3 6 9 12	D	100 95 90 85 80
B	0 25 50 75 100	E	200 170 140 110 80
C	14 20 26 32 38	F	1250 1150 1050 950 850

Go!

1	10 40 70 100 130
2	99,352
3	No, it should be: 0 9 18 27 36
4	70
5	Eight or 8 (£20 notes)

Negative Numbers 1 (p.30)

Check-in

1	0 2.5 5.2 7 9
2	1, 3 and 8

Set?

A	0 and 7	D	-5°C -4°C -2°C 1°C 3°C
B	-3, -1 and 4	E	-6°C -3°C 0°C 3°C 9°C
C	-6, -2 and 1	F	New York

Go!

1	-6 -2 2 6 10
2	Possible solutions: -1°C and -6°C or -2°C and -7°C etc.
3	No. -5°C is colder than 2°C
4	a) Thursday b) Wednesday c) 6°C
5	5 m

Negative Numbers 2 (p.32)

Check-in

1	-8 -5 -4 4 8
2	-2, 0 and 5

Set?

A	(i) -3	(ii) -2
B	(i) 4	(ii) 1
C	(i) -3	(ii) -8
D	(i) 8	(ii) 0
E	8	
F	9	

Go!

1	2 − 3 = -1 1 − 3 = -2
2	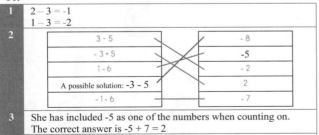
3	She has included -5 as one of the numbers when counting on. The correct answer is -5 + 7 = 2
4	5th (floor)
5	-8 (°C) and 7 (°C)

Mental Addition (p.34)

Check-in

1	80		700
	90		700
	90		900
	100		600
	80		600
	120		1,400

Set?

A	770	D	1,790	G	6,150
B	850	E	355	H	10,998
C	600	F	8,013		

Go!

1	11,106
2	Dani should have adjusted by subtracting 1 The correct answer is 1469
3	4,600 + 230 = 4,830
4	556
5	100 220 340 460 580

Mental Subtraction (p.36)

Check-in

1	30		700
	20		100
	30		500
	60		0

Set?

A	290	D	1,310	G	1,416
B	640	E	2	H	8,900
C	4	F	2,418		

Go!

1	8,892
2	5,001 − 4,998 = 3
3	You need to adjust by adding 1 not subtracting 1 The correct answer is 521
4	8 (visits)
5	4.003 − 3.998 → 4.602 − 4.300 4.300 − 3.998 → 4.023 − 4.018 4.030 − 3.998 → 4.060 − 4.028

Written Methods: Addition (p.38)

Check-in

1	23		124
2	492		741

Set?

A	91,619	D	49,923
B	129,200	E	64,991
C	179,796		

Go!

1	15,072 (miles)
2	2 7 **1** 2 7 + **4** 4 7 5 3 1 6 0 2
3	The total of the tens column should be 8 (2 + 5 + 1)
4	Statement ticked: 59,999 + 39,987

Written Methods: Subtraction (p.40)

Check-in

1	13		25
2	323		327

Set?

A	13,658	D	54,591
B	30,364	E	41,766
C	44,128		

Go!

1	24,156 (people)
2	4 1 **9** 2 1 − 4 6 1 6 3 7 3 0 5
3	She has subtracted 4 from 7 in the tens column and not exchanged first. The correct answer is 26,471
4	Largest difference = 97,742 (98,765 − 1,023) Smallest difference = 358 (10,234 − 9,876)

Multiples (p.42)

Check-in

1	Rings around: 20, 16 and 36
2	12 15 18 21 24
3	Rings around: 20 and 40

Set?

A	A possible solution: 6, 12, 18, 24, 30 etc.
B	A possible solution: 11, 22, 33, 44, 55 etc.
C	15, 30, 45, 60, 75
D	Three (32, 40 and 48)
E	Ticks against: 9, 21 and 45

Go!

1	Possible solutions: $15 + 6 = 21$, $10 + 18 = 28$, $25 + 24 = 49$
2	Possible reason: 4 is a factor of 12 not a multiple of 12
3	A possible solution: A = 12, B = 60, C = 20
4	1:20 p.m.

Factors (p.44)

Check-in

1	1 and 5
2	2 and 4
3	4 and 5

Set?

A	1, 2, 4 and 8
B	1, 3, 5 and 15
C	1, 2, 4, 8 and 16
D	1 and 2
E	Ticks against: 1 and 11

Go!

1	2 and 6, 4 and 8, 8 and 12
2	No, for example, 9 has three factors (1, 3 and 9) and 6 has four factors (1, 2, 3 and 6)
3	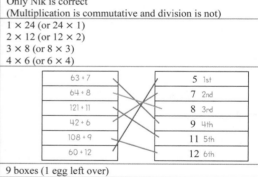
4	6 ($1 + 2 + 3 = 6$)
5	49

Prime Numbers (p.46)

Check-in

1	Ring around: 16
2	False
3	True
4	False
5	True

Set?

A	8	C	5,13 and 7,11	E	19 and 29
B	23 and 29	D	2		

Go!

1	23, 47, 59 or 29, 47, 53
2	No. A possible reason: 27 ends with 7 but is not a prime number
3	3 and 5, 5 and 7, 11 and 13, 17 and 19
4	A possible solution:

	Prime number	Multiple of 4
Factor of 8	2	8
Sum of the digits is 8	17	44

5	13, 17, 31, 37, 71 and 73

Square Numbers (p.48)

Check-in

1	1		36
2	Ring around: 121		
3	True		

Set?

A	Ticks against: 16 and 25				
B	(i) 4	C	(i) 1	D	100, 121 and 144
	(ii) 49		(ii) 9		
	(iii) 64		(iii) 36		
	(iv) 100		(iv) 81		

Go!

1	Possible solutions: $9 + 16 = 25$, $36 + 64 = 100$, $25 + 144 = 169$
2	No. 7^2 means 7×7 not 7×2 The correct answer is 49
3	48, 49, 50
4	8, 27, 64 and 125

Multiplication Tables (p.50)

Check-in

1	20		
2	True		
3	16		30
	30		6
	5		10

Set?

A	72	G	$72 \div 9 = 8$
B	49		$9 \times 8 = 72$
C	81		$72 \div 8 = 9$
D	132	H	
E	6		
F	9		

H

×	6	9	11
4	24	36	44
7	42	63	77
12	72	108	132

I

×	6	8	5	4	3
12	72	96	60	48	36
7	42	56	35	28	21
9	54	72	45	36	27
11	66	88	55	44	33
6	36	48	30	24	18

Go!

1

×	6	8	3
3	18	24	9
7	42	56	21
8	48	64	24

2	Only Nik is correct (Multiplication is commutative and division is not)
3	1×24 (or 24×1) 2×12 (or 12×2) 3×8 (or 8×3) 4×6 (or 6×4)

4

$63 \div 7$	5 1st
$64 \div 8$	7 2nd
$121 \div 11$	8 3rd
$42 \div 6$	9 4th
$108 \div 9$	11 5th
$60 \div 12$	12 6th

5	9 boxes (1 egg left over)

Multiplying by 10 or 100 Part 1 (p.52)

Check-in

1	40	2	50
3	60	4	70
5	80	6	100
7	110	8	120

Set?

A	(i) 350	C	(i) 6,700	E	2,700
	(ii) 510		(ii) 4,300		
	(iii) 700		(iii) 5,800		
	(iv) 940		(iv) 9,600		
B	(i) 2,980	D	(i) 16,700	F	31,600
	(ii) 5,710		(ii) 40,300		
	(iii) 6,000		(iii) 58,000		
	(iv) 8,010		(iv) 10,000		

Go!

1	604
2	(£)13 or (£)13.00
3	No, the correct answer is 3,060
4	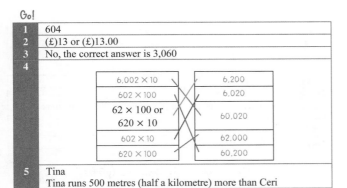

5	Tina
	Tina runs 500 metres (half a kilometre) more than Ceri

Multiplying by 10 or 100 Part 2 (p.54)

Check-in

1	3600
2	Ring around: 240
3	Two tenths or 2 tenths or 0.2
4	Seven hundredths or 7 hundredths or 0.07

Set?

A	32	D	20.3	G	4,050.6
B	1.7	E	2.03	H	320.4
C	460	F	30.2		

Go!

1	Ring around: 705
2	850 (cm)
3	No, the correct answer is 120
4	Sometimes true, for example: 1.45 × 100 = 145 and 1.4 × 100 = 140
5	Boxes ticked: 0.62 × 10 and 0.062 × 100

Dividing by 10 or 100 Part 1 (p.56)

Check-in

1	6	2	8
3	5	4	4
5	7	6	10
7	12	8	11

Set?

A	(i) 24	C	(i) 2.43	E	305
	(ii) 57		(ii) 5.67		
	(iii) 78		(iii) 7.08	F	3.4
	(iv) 91		(iv) 9.23		
B	(i) 360.1	D	(i) 90.03	G	20.21
	(ii) 570.8		(ii) 26.71		
	(iii) 27.8		(iii) 47.08		
	(iv) 9.1		(iv) 170.5		

Go!

1	560
2	56 (p)
3	Always true, for example: 5000 ÷ 100 can be worked out by 5000 ÷ 10 = 500 followed by 500 ÷ 10 = 50
4	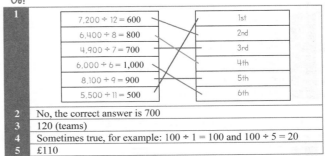
5	250 (ml)

Dividing by 10 or 100 Part 2 (p.58)

Check-in

1	12
2	Ring around: 30.4
3	Five hundredths or 5 hundredths or 0.05
4	Seven thousandths or 7 thousandths or 0.007

Set?

A	0.38	D	0.002	G	0.009
B	7.03	E	0.021	H	3.246
C	0.314	F	3.723		

Go!

1	560
2	Shop A. A possible reason: Shop A = 12.5p per pen and Shop B = 13.5p per pen
3	No, the correct answer is 4.005
4	Boxes ticked: 0.23 ÷ 10 and 2.3 ÷ 100
5	÷100 ×10 ×100

Mental Multiplication (p.60)

Check-in

1	12		28		48
	18		81		96
	16		36		56
	99		9		84
	72		24		24
	36		64		33
	21		88		36

Set?

A	280	C	1,800	E	1,800
B	480	D	8,100	F	960

Go!

1	70 × 80 = 5,600 (or 80 × 70 = 5,600)
2	Yes
	6 × 5 × 100 = 30 × 100 = 3,000
3	360 (pupils)
4	Boxes ticked: 9 × 120 and 300 × 4
5	£8,400

Mental Division (p.62)

Check-in

1	9	2	9
3	6	4	7
5	7	6	10
7	11	8	7

Set?

A	80	D	600	G	120
B	90	E	700	H	110
C	90	F	1,200	I	6,000

Go!

1	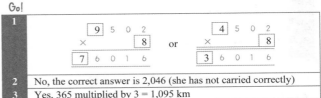
2	No, the correct answer is 700
3	120 (teams)
4	Sometimes true, for example: 100 ÷ 1 = 100 and 100 ÷ 5 = 20
5	£110

Written Methods: Multiplication 1 (p.64)

Check-in

1	13		17
2	400 50 6		
3	62		200
4	Ring around: 130		

Set?

A	693	D	6,936	G	27,426
B	2,884	E	9,852	H	28,624
C	4,134	F	77,886	I	77,436

Go!

1	9 5 0 2 × 8 or 4 5 0 2 × 8
	7 6 0 1 6 3 6 0 1 6
2	No, the correct answer is 2,046 (she has not carried correctly)
3	Yes, 365 multiplied by 3 = 1,095 km
4	4,734
5	(£)7,470

Written Methods: Multiplication 2 (p.66)

Check-in

1	936	2	1,484
3	4,269	4	36,078

Set?

A	759	C	8,442	E	6,573
B	2,448	D	51,604	F	544,448

Go!

1	No, she has not placed a zero when multiplying by 10. The correct answer is 2,881
2	Yes. 17 × 124 = 2,108 and 2,108 is greater than 2,000
3	36,771
4	(£)39.00 or (£)39

Written Methods: Division 1 (p.68)

Check-in

1	Ring around: 2 r 1		
2	Ring around: 3 r 2		
3	2 r 3	4	2 r 6

Set?

A	113	D	2,823	G	823
B	185	E	1,701	H	555
C	115	F	1,315	I	677

Go!

1	123
2	No, he did not exchange the remainder. The correct answer is 268
3	$\begin{array}{c} \quad 2\ 3\ 1\ 9 \\ 4\ \overline{)\ 9\ 2\ 7\ 6} \end{array}$
4	78 full boxes, 2 eggs left over

Written Methods: Division 2 (p.70)

Check-in

1	214	2	121
3	1,497	4	254

Set?

A	45	D	146	G	76
B	55	E	264	H	134
C	28	F	197	I	25

Go!

1	28 (coaches)
2	$414 \div 18 = 23$
3	No. The 2 in the quotient is placed incorrectly. The correct answer is 24
4	Sometimes true, for example: 1,080 ÷ 12 = 90 and 9,990 ÷ 90 = 111
5	2,624 ÷ 16 = 164 and because 32 = 2 × 16, 164 ÷ 2 = 82

Adding Decimals (p.72)

Check-in

1	923	2	1,175
3	5,315	4	11,882

Set?

A	76.19	D	16.085
B	11.590	E	25.116
C	126.79		

Go!

1	1.01 and 18.99
2	(£)124.63
3	$\begin{array}{r} 7\ 2.3\ 5 \\ +\ \ 4\ 4.4\ 4 \\ \hline 1\ 1\ 6.7\ 9 \end{array}$
4	The decimal points have not been lined up correctly. The correct answer is 28.677
5	44.35 (km)

Subtracting Decimals (p.74)

Check-in

1	263	2	219
3	526	4	915

Set?

A	40.66	D	4.43
B	1.267	E	16.808
C	4.44		

Go!

1	7.485 (km)
2	$12.1 - 3.65 = 8.45$
3	Zeroes have not been used as placeholders (she should have written 28.400). The correct answer is 12.684
4	(£)66.05

Multiplication with Decimals (p.76)

Check-in

1	24		15
	48		42
2	105		162

Set?

A	0.6	C	2.4	E	10.5
B	1.5	D	4.8	F	16.2

Go!

1	0.5
2	No, 7 × 9 = 63 and 0.7 is ten times smaller than 7 so the correct answer is 6.3
3	(£)1.40
4	400 (ml)
5	(see matching below)

$1.4 \times 4 = 5.6$	1st
$0.6 \times 7 = 4.2$	2nd
$9 \times 0.5 = 4.5$	3rd
$2.4 \times 2 = 4.8$	4th
$0.7 \times 7 = 4.9$	5th

Equivalent Fractions (p.78)

Check-in

1	Rings around: $\frac{4}{5}$ $\frac{4}{10}$ $\frac{4}{3}$
2	Fractions ticked: $\frac{2}{5}$ $\frac{7}{5}$
3	Any one square shaded
4	Any two squares shaded

Set?

A	Possible solutions: $\frac{4}{12}$ $\frac{8}{24}$ $\frac{1}{3}$	C	(i) $\frac{2}{3} = \frac{8}{12}$ (ii) $\frac{3}{5} = \frac{24}{40}$ (iii) $\frac{3}{8} = \frac{150}{400}$	E	$\frac{8}{15}$ $\frac{5}{10}$ $\frac{9}{20}$ $\frac{2}{5}$
B	(i) $\frac{1}{2} = \frac{3}{6}$ (ii) $\frac{1}{3} = \frac{2}{6}$ (iii) $\frac{1}{5} = \frac{100}{500}$	D	$\frac{3}{8}$ $\frac{7}{16}$ $\frac{1}{2}$ $\frac{3}{4}$		

Go!

1	Tina, $\frac{15}{21}$ is greater than $\frac{14}{21}$
2	No, he should multiply or divide to find equivalent fractions
3	$\frac{5}{6}$ $\frac{7}{9}$ $\frac{3}{4}$ $\frac{2}{3}$ $\frac{5}{12}$
4	$\frac{1+2}{4} = \frac{9}{12} = \frac{27}{30+6}$
5	Possible solutions: $\frac{1}{4} = \frac{2}{8} = \frac{9}{36}$ or $\frac{2}{4} = \frac{3}{6} = \frac{9}{18}$ or $\frac{3}{4} = \frac{6}{8} = \frac{9}{12}$

Simplifying Fractions (p.80)

Check-in

1	1, 2, 3, 4, 6, 8, 12, 24
2	Rings around: 1 2 4 8
3	False, 30 is a common multiple of 5 and 10
4	Ring around: 4

Set?

A	Boxes ticked: $\frac{5}{15}$ $\frac{3}{12}$ $\frac{8}{18}$ $\frac{14}{21}$ $\frac{25}{100}$
B	Boxes ticked: $\frac{3}{9} = \frac{1}{3}$ $\frac{8}{20} = \frac{2}{5}$ $\frac{16}{40} = \frac{2}{5}$

C	(i)	$\frac{1}{3}$
	(ii)	$\frac{1}{5}$
	(iii)	$\frac{3}{20}$
	(iv)	$\frac{5}{6}$
D	(i)	$\frac{1}{4}$
	(ii)	$\frac{2}{5}$
	(iii)	$\frac{2}{5}$
	(iv)	$\frac{3}{10}$

Go!

1	Sometimes true. $\frac{8}{12}$ can be simplified by halving both numerator and denominator to $\frac{4}{6}$ and $\frac{2}{3}$ but $\frac{9}{12}$ would need both numerator and denominator dividing by 3
2	She has not found a common factor of the numerator and denominator. The correct answer is: $\frac{12}{26} = \frac{6}{13}$
3	Any fifteen triangles shaded
4	$\frac{27}{72}$
5	29

Mixed Numbers (p.82)

Check-in

1	$\frac{1}{4}$		$\frac{1}{3}$
	$\frac{1}{5}$		$\frac{5}{5}$ or 1
2	1 r 2	3	1 r 2
4	2 r 1	5	3 r 1

Set?

A	$1\frac{2}{5}$	D	$3\frac{1}{5}$	G	$\frac{7}{2}$
B	$1\frac{2}{7}$	E	$\frac{11}{6}$	H	$\frac{38}{9}$
C	$2\frac{1}{4}$	F	$\frac{12}{5}$		

Go!

1	$\frac{11}{8}$ $1\frac{1}{2}$ $\frac{11}{6}$ $\frac{10}{3}$
2	$\frac{15}{7} = 2\frac{1}{7}$
3	The denominator should remain unchanged. The correct answer is $\frac{8}{5} = 1\frac{3}{5}$
4	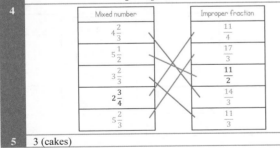
5	3 (cakes)

Fraction of an Amount (p.84)

Check-in

1	$\frac{3}{4}$		$\frac{2}{3}$
	$\frac{3}{5}$		$\frac{5}{6}$
2	8	3	5
4	10	5	11

Set?

A	8	D	25
B	20	E	55
C	45	F	61

Go!

1	18 (girls)
2	No, she should have divided by the denominator and multiplied by the numerator. The correct answer is 8 (12 ÷ 3 = 4, 4 × 2 = 8)

3	$\frac{2}{5}$ of 40 = 16
4	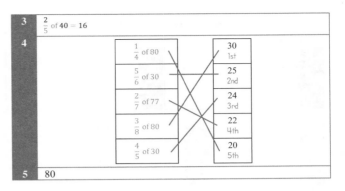
5	80

Adding Fractions 1 (p.86)

Check-in

1	Any one box shaded
2	Any four boxes shaded
3	$\frac{5}{9}$
4	Ring around: $1\frac{3}{4}$

Set?

A	$\frac{2}{3}$	D	$\frac{4}{5}$	G	$1\frac{1}{4}$
B	$\frac{4}{5}$	E	$\frac{7}{9}$	H	$1\frac{2}{9}$
C	$\frac{5}{7}$	F	$\frac{6}{7}$		

Go!

1	$\frac{4}{8}$ or $\frac{1}{2}$
2	$\frac{2}{3} + \frac{5}{3} = \frac{7}{3}$
3	He has added the denominators. The correct answer is $\frac{5}{6}$
4	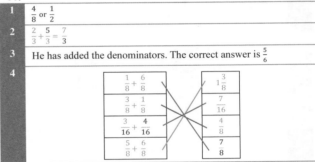

Adding Fractions 2 (p.88)

Check-in

1	False. The correct answer is $\frac{3}{5}$
2	Rings around: $\frac{2}{6}$ and $\frac{3}{9}$
3	Rings around: $\frac{6}{10}$ and $\frac{9}{15}$
4	$1\frac{7}{12}$

Set?

A	$\frac{3}{6}$ or $\frac{1}{2}$	D	$\frac{11}{15}$	G	$\frac{11}{20}$
B	$\frac{3}{10}$	E	$\frac{8}{9}$	H	$\frac{7}{12}$
C	$\frac{3}{8}$	F	$\frac{7}{8}$		

Go!

1	$1\frac{7}{12}$ (km)
2	Possible solution: $\frac{1}{3} + \frac{4}{9} = \frac{7}{9}$
3	$\frac{7}{10}$
4	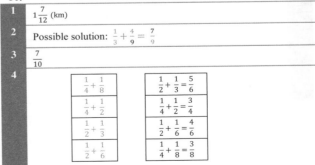

Adding Mixed Numbers (p.90)

Check-in

1	$\frac{3}{7}$		$\frac{3}{10}$
2	$1\frac{1}{3}$		$1\frac{2}{9}$
	$1\frac{4}{8}$		$1\frac{1}{6}$

Set?

A	$1\frac{3}{7}$	D	$2\frac{7}{9}$	G	$4\frac{1}{3}$
B	$2\frac{3}{5}$	E	$2\frac{3}{10}$	H	$4\frac{3}{8}$
C	$1\frac{9}{10}$	F	$2\frac{7}{12}$		

Go!

1	$1\frac{2}{7} + 2\frac{3}{7} = 3\frac{5}{7}$
2	He has not found and used a common denominator. The correct answer is $2\frac{3}{6}$ $(= 2\frac{1}{2})$
3	$1\frac{1}{4}, 1\frac{1}{2}, 1\frac{3}{4}, 2, 2\frac{1}{4}$
4	$3\frac{4}{10}$ or $3\frac{2}{5}$ (km)

Subtracting Mixed Numbers (p.96)

Check-in

1	$\frac{2}{5}$		$\frac{1}{5}$
	$\frac{5}{9}$		$\frac{4}{9}$
	$\frac{4}{8} = \frac{1}{2}$		$\frac{1}{8}$

Set?

A	$1\frac{2}{5}$	D	$1\frac{5}{9}$	G	$1\frac{5}{8}$
B	$2\frac{5}{8}$	E	$2\frac{1}{5}$	H	$1\frac{7}{8}$
C	$\frac{5}{7}$	F	$\frac{7}{9}$		

Go!

1	$2\frac{2}{7} - 1\frac{3}{7} = \frac{6}{7}$
2	No, she has subtracted the proper fractions in the wrong order. The correct answer is $1\frac{2}{5}$
3	$2\frac{2}{9}$ or $1\frac{5}{9}$
4	$1\frac{3}{4}$

Subtracting Fractions 1 (p.92)

Check-in

1	Any four boxes shaded
2	Any five boxes shaded
3	$\frac{4}{7}$
4	

Set?

A	$\frac{3}{5}$	D	$\frac{2}{5}$	G	$\frac{2}{3}$
B	$\frac{3}{7}$	E	$\frac{4}{11}$	H	$\frac{7}{13}$
C	$\frac{4}{9}$	F	$\frac{3}{8}$		

Go!

1	$\frac{6}{10}$ or $\frac{3}{5}$
2	$\frac{13}{12} - \frac{9}{12} = \frac{4}{12}$
3	1 is equal to $\frac{5}{5}$ and $\frac{5}{5} - \frac{1}{5} = \frac{4}{5}$
4	Box ticked: $\frac{8}{5}$ and $\frac{7}{5}$

Subtracting Fractions 2 (p.94)

Check-in

1	$\frac{2}{8}$ or $\frac{1}{4}$
2	Rings around: $\frac{2}{4}$, $\frac{3}{6}$ and $\frac{4}{8}$
3	Rings around: $\frac{6}{8}$ and $\frac{9}{12}$

Set?

A	$\frac{1}{8}$	D	$\frac{3}{8}$	G	$\frac{7}{12}$
B	$\frac{1}{10}$	E	$\frac{4}{9}$	H	$\frac{7}{20}$
C	$\frac{2}{9}$	F	$\frac{1}{12}$		

Go!

1	$\frac{7}{20}$
2	$\frac{2}{3}$ and $\frac{8}{9}$
3	She has subtracted the denominators rather than using a common denominator. The correct answer is $\frac{4}{12}$ or $\frac{2}{6}$ or $\frac{1}{3}$
4	$\frac{3}{10}$ and $\frac{12}{10}$ (or $\frac{6}{5}$ or $1\frac{1}{5}$)

Multiplying a Fraction (p.98)

Check-in

1	False (it is $2\frac{1}{4}$)
2	True
3	Ring around: $2\frac{3}{5}$

Set?

A	(i) $\frac{4}{5}$		C	(i) $\frac{44}{9}$ or $4\frac{8}{9}$
	(ii) $\frac{3}{7}$			(ii) $\frac{32}{5}$ or $6\frac{2}{5}$
	(iii) $\frac{5}{8}$			(iii) $\frac{69}{10}$ or $6\frac{9}{10}$
B	(i) $2\frac{2}{5}$		D	(i) $\frac{36}{5}$ or $7\frac{1}{5}$
	(ii) $1\frac{7}{9}$			(ii) $\frac{52}{7}$ or $7\frac{3}{7}$
	(iii) $1\frac{1}{4}$			(iii) $\frac{44}{4}$ or 11

Go!

1	Possible solutions: $\frac{1}{9} \times 6 = \frac{6}{9}$ $\frac{6}{9} \times 1 = \frac{6}{9}$
2	No, only the numerator should have been multiplied by 3. The correct answer is $\frac{9}{5}$ (or $1\frac{4}{5}$)

3	$1\frac{1}{3} \times 2$	$1\frac{1}{3} \times 2 = 2\frac{2}{3}$
	$\frac{7}{9} \times 4$	$\frac{7}{9} \times 4 = 3\frac{1}{9}$
	$1\frac{5}{6} \times 2$	$\frac{2}{3} \times 5 = 3\frac{1}{3}$
	$\frac{2}{3} \times 5$	$1\frac{5}{6} \times 2 = 3\frac{2}{3}$

4	Dave ($20 \times 1\frac{3}{5} = 32$) 32 kilometres > 30 kilometres

Multiplying Fractions (p.100)

Check-in

1	25		24
	8		40
2	$\frac{2}{5}$		
3	False ($\frac{9}{15} = \frac{3}{5}$)		

Set?

A	(i) $\frac{1}{20}$		C	(i) $\frac{8}{15}$	
	(ii) $\frac{1}{12}$			(ii) $\frac{4}{25}$	
	(iii) $\frac{1}{9}$			(iii) $\frac{9}{16}$	
B	(i) $\frac{2}{15}$		D	(i) $\frac{1}{4}$	(ii) $\frac{1}{10}$
	(ii) $\frac{3}{8}$			(iii) $\frac{5}{12}$	(iv) $\frac{1}{4}$
	(iii) $\frac{2}{9}$				

Go!

1	A possible solution: $\frac{1}{4} \times \frac{2}{3} = \frac{1}{6}$
2	No, you do not need to use a common denominator to multiply fractions
3	$\frac{4}{9}$
4	Calculations ticked: $\frac{1}{2} \times \frac{1}{2}$ and $\frac{4}{5} \times \frac{1}{3}$
5	250 (ml)

Dividing a Fraction (p.102)

Check-in

1	$\frac{1}{3} = \frac{3}{9}$		$\frac{3}{5} = \frac{6}{10}$		$\frac{3}{4} = \frac{6}{8}$
	$\frac{5}{6} = \frac{15}{18}$		$\frac{1}{4} = \frac{4}{16}$		$\frac{1}{5} = \frac{3}{15}$
2	$\frac{2}{3} = \frac{4}{6} = \frac{8}{12}$				

Set?

A	(i) $\frac{1}{7}$		C	(i) $\frac{3}{10}$
	(ii) $\frac{1}{5}$			(ii) $\frac{3}{8}$
	(iii) $\frac{1}{9}$			(iii) $\frac{5}{18}$
B	(i) $\frac{1}{10}$		D	(i) $\frac{1}{36}$ (ii) $\frac{5}{48}$
	(ii) $\frac{1}{6}$			(iii) $\frac{2}{75}$ (iv) $\frac{3}{130}$
	(iii) $\frac{1}{16}$			

Go!

1	Possible solutions: $\frac{1}{4} \times \frac{1}{3} = \frac{1}{12}$ or $\frac{1}{3} \times \frac{1}{4} = \frac{1}{12}$ $\frac{1}{3} \div 4 = \frac{1}{12}$ or $\frac{1}{4} \div 3 = \frac{1}{12}$
2	No, the correct answer is $\frac{1}{12}$
3	$\frac{1}{3} \div 5 = \frac{1}{15}$ or $\frac{1}{5} \div 3 = \frac{1}{15}$
4	

$\frac{4}{9} \div 2$	$\frac{1}{5} \div 2 = \frac{1}{10}$
$\frac{1}{5} \div 2$	$\frac{1}{3} \div 3 = \frac{1}{9}$
$\frac{1}{3} \div 3$	$\frac{4}{9} \div 2 = \frac{2}{9}$
$\frac{6}{7} \div 3$	$\frac{6}{7} \div 3 = \frac{2}{7}$

5	15 (cm) because $\frac{3}{5} \div 4 = \frac{3}{20}$ and $\frac{3}{20}$ of 1 metre = 15 cm

Fractions and Decimals (p.104)

Check-in

1	0.1
2	0.01
3	A possible solution: $\frac{9}{10}$
4	A possible solution: $\frac{7}{100}$
5	$\frac{1}{5} = \frac{2}{10}$	$\frac{3}{20} = \frac{15}{100}$

Set?

A	0.8		D	0.44
B	0.55		E	$\frac{1}{20}$
C	$\frac{17}{100}$		F	$\frac{4}{25}$

Go!

1	$\frac{1}{50}$ 0.15 $\frac{1}{5}$ $\frac{51}{100}$ 1.5
2	For example: $\frac{9}{20} = \frac{45}{100} = 0.45$ which is not 9.20
3	$\frac{3}{20} = 0.15$
4	Any nine squares shaded
5	Val $\frac{13}{20} = 0.65$ which is greater than 0.625 of a kilometre

Fractions, Decimals and Percentages (p.106)

Set?

A	$\frac{3}{100}$ and 0.03
B	$\frac{90}{100}$ (or $\frac{9}{10}$) and 0.9
C	$\frac{23}{100}$ and 23%
D	$\frac{33}{100}$ and 33%
E	0.6 and 60%

Go!

1	4% 0.4 $\frac{45}{100}$ $\frac{5}{10}$ 4.5
2	3% = 0.03 (= $\frac{3}{100}$) and 0.3 = 30% (= $\frac{30}{100}$)
3	$\frac{1}{4} = 25\%$
4	Kitty $\frac{17}{20} = \frac{85}{100} = 85\%$ and 85% is greater than 68%
5	£10

Percentage of an Amount 1 (p.108)

Check-in

1	6		12
	18		2.4
2	35		12
	14		13
	39		45

Set?

A	12		D	£7
B	12		E	£6.50
C	60		F	90 kg

Go!

1	£180
2	25% of 10 = 10% of 25
3	Box ticked: 10% of £135
4	George 75% of 80 = 60 marks and 60 > 57
5	75% of £48 = £36

Percentage of an Amount 2 (p.110)

Check-in

1	$\frac{3}{10}$		$\frac{1}{2}$
	$\frac{7}{10}$		$\frac{9}{10}$
2	3		30
	15		4.5

Set?

A	£14		D	£27
B	4 kg		E	£190
C	£7.50		F	204 cm

Go!

1	65% of 20 = 13
2	No. To find 20% she needs to find 10% first (= £8) then multiply by 2 (20% of £80 = £16)
3	300 ml
4	£40
5	B 15% of 30 = 4.5 and 30% of 15 = 4.5

Percentage of an Amount 3 (p.112)

Check-in

1	2		6
2	False. We divide by 5		
3	4		2
	8		18

Set?

A	£12		D	495 m
B	54 kg		E	98 litres
C	6		F	£399

Go!

1	11% of 200 = 22
2	86% of 50 = 43
3	No, he needs to find 1% first (1% = £0.60) then multiply by 9. The correct answer is £5.40
4	£85.50
5	51% of 200 > 24% of 400

Time 1 (p.114)

Check-in

1	2 o'clock	Half past 4	Quarter to 6	
2	I II III IV V VI VII VIII IX X XI XII			

Set?

A	
	(i) 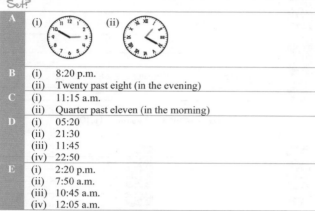 (ii)

B	
	(i) 8:20 p.m.
	(ii) Twenty past eight (in the evening)

C	
	(i) 11:15 a.m.
	(ii) Quarter past eleven (in the morning)

D	
	(i) 05:20
	(ii) 21:30
	(iii) 11:45
	(iv) 22:50

E	
	(i) 2:20 p.m.
	(ii) 7:50 a.m.
	(iii) 10:45 a.m.
	(iv) 12:05 a.m.

Go!

1	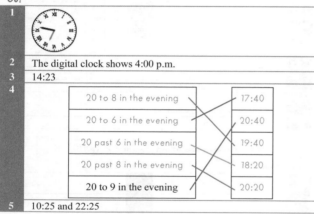
2	The digital clock shows 4:00 p.m.
3	14:23
4	20 to 8 in the evening — 17:40 20 to 6 in the evening — 20:40 20 past 6 in the evening — 19:40 20 past 8 in the evening — 18:20 20 to 9 in the evening — 20:20
5	10:25 and 22:25

Time 2 (p.116)

Check-in

1	06:40		19:30
2	4:35 p.m.		6:20 a.m.
3	False. There are 60 minutes in 1 hour		
4	5:55 p.m.		

Set?

A	Start time	Finish time	Duration
	3:15 p.m.	4:30 p.m.	1 hour 15 minutes
	4:45 p.m.	5:10 p.m.	25 minutes
	5:50 p.m.	6:25 p.m.	35 minutes
	6:05 p.m.	7:55 p.m.	1 hour 50 minutes

B	Start time	Finish time	Duration
	07:23	08:15	52 minutes
	10:35	11:15	40 minutes
	13:47	15:12	1 hour 25 minutes
	14:14	15:07	53 minutes

C	
	(i) 1 hour
	(ii) 3
	(iii) 14:28

Go!

1	5:50 p.m.
2	No, the correct answer is 35 minutes
3	A possible solution: The time between 01:30 and 02:15 is 45 minutes

---

4	a) 34 minutes
	b) 17:20 (5:20 p.m.)
5	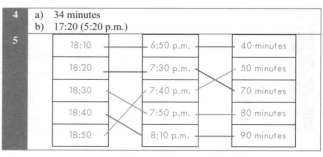

18:10 — 6:50 p.m. — 40 minutes
18:20 — 7:30 p.m. — 50 minutes
18:30 — 7:40 p.m. — 70 minutes
18:40 — 7:50 p.m. — 80 minutes
18:50 — 8:10 p.m. — 90 minutes

Converting Metric Units 1 (p.118)

Check-in

1		
	170	2,500
	3,500	16
	60	7
	32	6.05
	1.9	6.5

Set?

A	cm	mm
	7	70
	4	40
	1.8	18
	3.52	35.2
	0.9	9

C	cm	m
	100	1
	200	2
	350	3.5
	125	1.25
	75	0.75

B	cm	mm
	1	10
	6	60
	2.5	25
	3.6	36
	0.8	8

D	m	km
	1,000	1
	3,000	3
	2,500	2.5
	3,200	3.2
	645	0.645

E	
	(i) 1,050 (metres)
	(ii) 302 (centimetres)
	(iii) 4 (millimetres)
	(iv) 0.95 (m)

Go!

1	0.85 (m)
2	No. 1.2 cm = 12 mm (because 1 cm = 10 mm)
3	25 (laps)
4	750 (m)

Converting Metric Units 2 (p.120)

Check-in

1		
	5	7.5
	4.025	0.325
	1,425	2,750
	4,500	800

Set?

A	kg	g
	1	1,000
	4	4,000
	3	3,000
	2.5	2,500
	4.5	4,500

B	g	kg
	1,200	1.2
	2,750	2.75
	3,450	3.45
	675	0.675
	400	0.4

C	litre	ml
	1	1,000
	3	3,000
	6	6,000
	6.3	6,300
	1.48	1,480

D	ml	litre
	1,400	1.4
	2,750	2.75
	1,350	1.35
	720	0.72
	2,045	2.045

E	1,005 (grams)
F	3.02 (litres)

Go!

1	5 (cups)
2	No. Half a litre = 500 ml, so 500 – 40 = 460 ml left
3	13 (plant pots)
4	A possible solution: 1,000 g 1.23 kg 1450 g $1\frac{1}{2}$ kg 1.6 kg
5	9 (litres)

2D Shapes (p.122)

Check-in

1
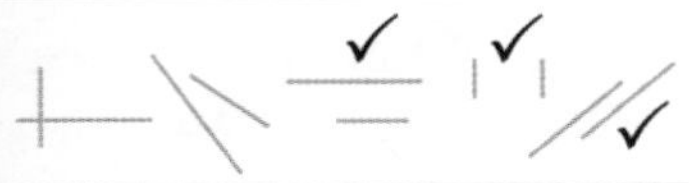

2
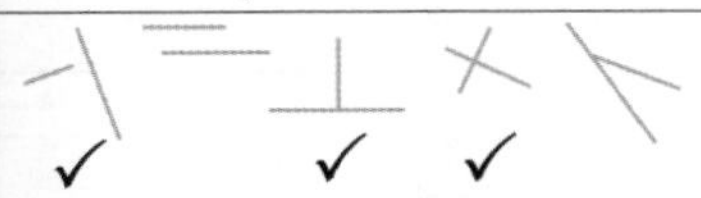

3
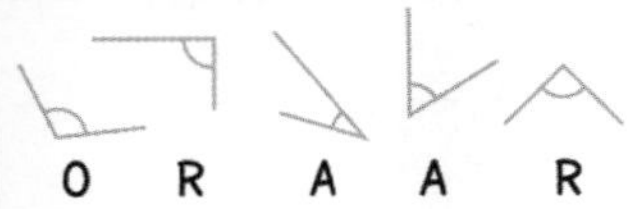

Set?

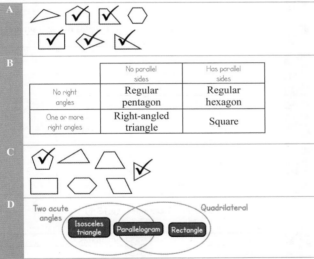

A
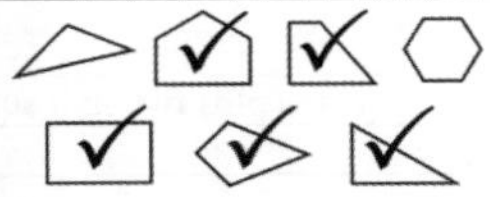

B

	No parallel sides	Has parallel sides
No right angles	Regular pentagon	Regular hexagon
One or more right angles	Right-angled triangle	Square

C
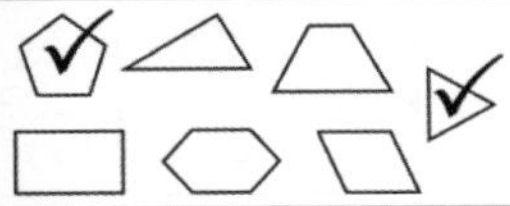

D
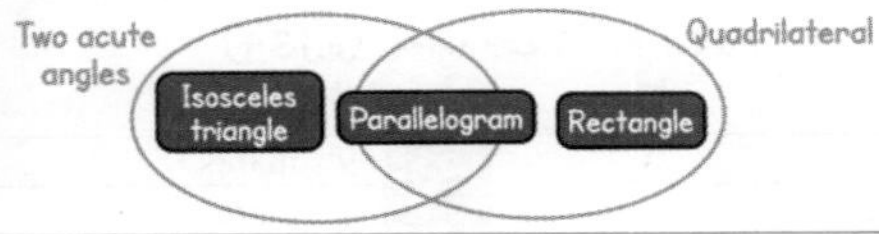

Go!

1
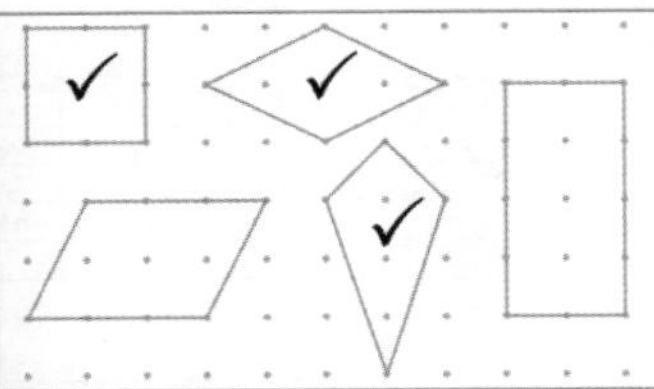

2 For example:
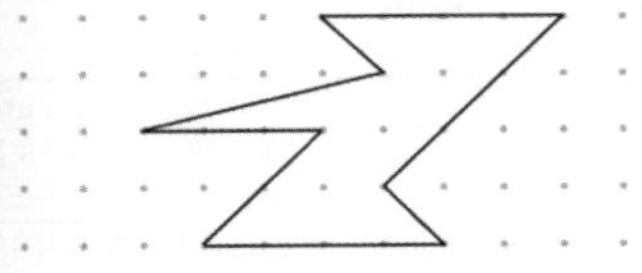

3
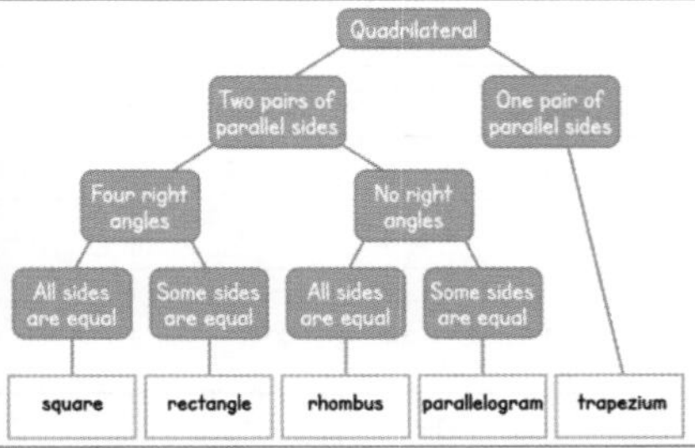

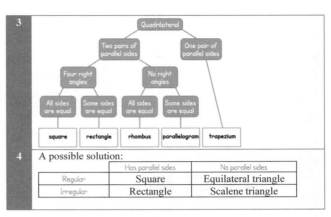

4 A possible solution:

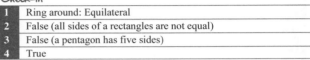

	Has parallel sides	No parallel sides
Regular	Square	Equilateral triangle
Irregular	Rectangle	Scalene triangle

Line Symmetry (p.124)

Check-in

1	Ring around: Equilateral
2	False (all sides of a rectangles are not equal)
3	False (a pentagon has five sides)
4	True

Set?

A
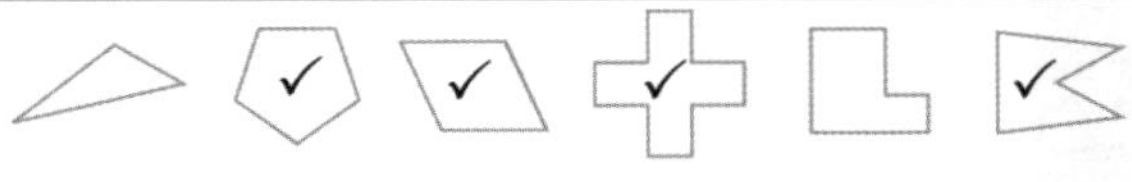

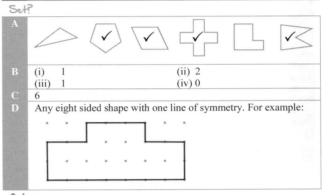

B (i) 1 (ii) 2
(iii) 1 (iv) 0

C 6

D Any eight sided shape with one line of symmetry. For example:
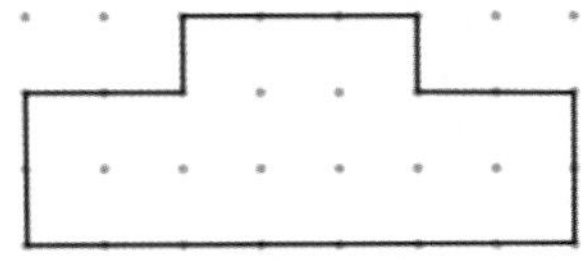

Go!

1
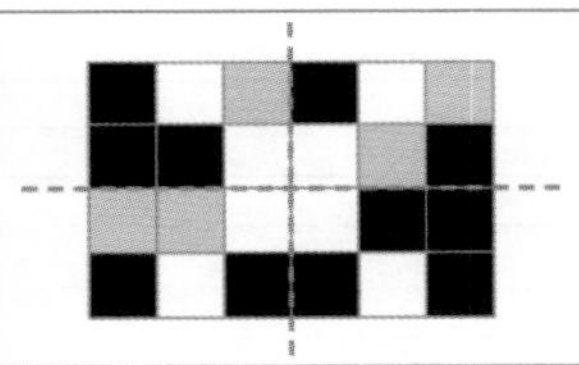

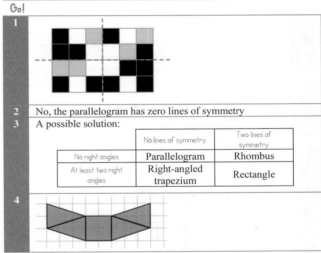

2 No, the parallelogram has zero lines of symmetry

3 A possible solution:

	No lines of symmetry	Two lines of symmetry
No right angles	Parallelogram	Rhombus
At least two right angles	Right-angled trapezium	Rectangle

4
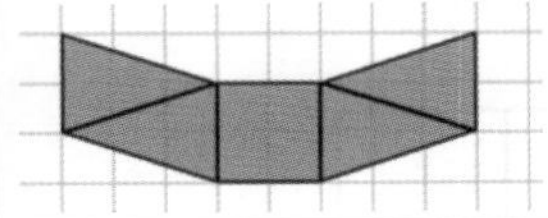

3D Shapes 1 (p.126)

Check-in

1
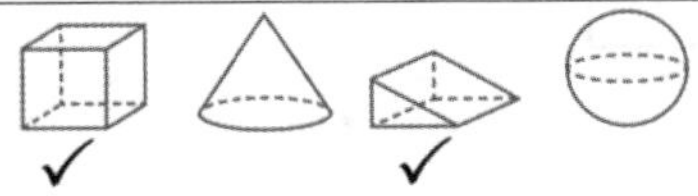

2
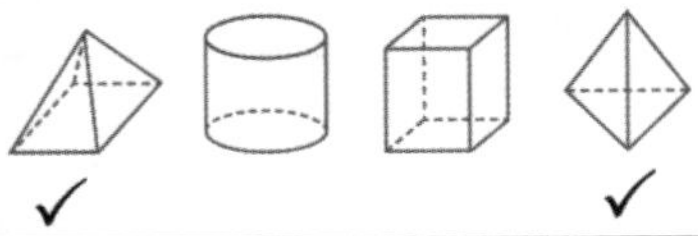

3 Cube, Cone, Triangular prism, Sphere
Square based pyramid, Cylinder, Cuboid, Triangular based pyramid

A

3D shape	Number of faces	Number of edges	Number of vertices
Triangular prism	5	9	6
Triangular-based pyramid	4	6	4
Square-based pyramid	5	8	5
Hexagonal prism	8	18	12
Hexagonal-based pyramid	7	12	7

B

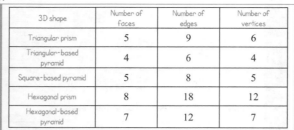

C

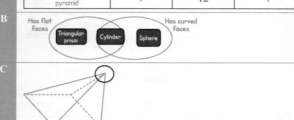

Go!

1	Hexagonal-based pyramid and pentagonal prism
2	A possible solution:

	Even number of faces	Odd number of faces
Even number of edges	Cube/cuboid	Square-based pyramid
Even number of vertices	Cube/cuboid	Triangular prism

3	No, he is incorrect. The pyramid has 5 faces, 8 edges and 5 vertices
4	Always true. There is a face for each edge of the base plus 1 (the base itself) and there is a vertex for each edge of the base plus 1 (the vertex at the top)

3D Shapes 2 (p.128)

Check-in

1	False (they have rectangular faces too)
2	True
3	False (they have triangular faces too)
4	True

Set?

A

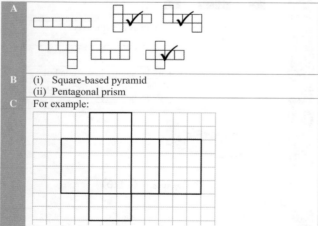

B	(i) Square-based pyramid
	(ii) Pentagonal prism
C	For example:

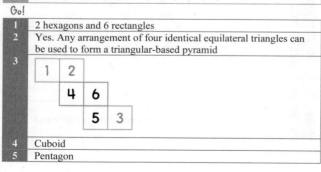

Go!

1	2 hexagons and 6 rectangles
2	Yes. Any arrangement of four identical equilateral triangles can be used to form a triangular-based pyramid
3	

```
1  2
   4  6
      5  3
```

4	Cuboid
5	Pentagon

Perimeter (p.130)

Check-in

1	18
2	26
3	3
4	15
5	True

Set?

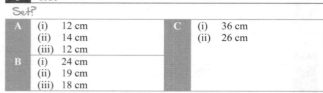

A	(i) 12 cm	C	(i) 36 cm
	(ii) 14 cm		(ii) 26 cm
	(iii) 12 cm		
B	(i) 24 cm		
	(ii) 19 cm		
	(iii) 18 cm		

Go!

1	9 cm
2	She has not found the total distance around the shape. The correct answer is $5 + 5 + 8 + 8 = 26$ cm
3	Box ticked: A regular pentagon with side length 5 cm. Because $5 \times 5 = 25$ cm (which is bigger than $6 \times 4 = 24$ cm)
4	£7.50

Area (p.132)

Check-in

1	1	2
2		

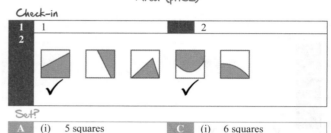

Set?

A	(i) 5 squares	C	(i) 6 squares
	(ii) 8 squares		(ii) 5 squares
	(iii) 6 squares		(iii) 12 squares
B	(i) 6 squares		
	(ii) 9 squares		
	(iii) 6 squares		

Go!

1	Three rectangles with sides of: 1 and 12, 2 and 6, 3 and 4
2	No. The area is 4 squares (3 whole squares plus two half squares)
3	23 to 25 squares
4	

Shape	Area
A	$3\frac{1}{2}$ squares
B	4 squares
C	7 squares
D	4.5 squares
E	6 squares

Area of Rectangles (p.134)

Check-in

1	8 squares	9 squares
	10 squares	5 squares
2	21	24	25

Set?

A	(i) 12 cm²
	(ii) 21 mm²
	(iii) 24 m²
B	(i) 9 cm²
	(ii) 25 cm²

C

Width	Length	Area
5 cm	8 cm	40 cm²
4 m	6 m	24 m²
4 cm	9 cm	36 cm²
1 mm	17 mm	17 mm²

Go!

1	9 cm
2	No, she has worked out the perimeter. The correct answer is 44 cm²
3	Sometimes true. For example: 4 cm by 6 cm will have an area (24 cm²) greater than the perimeter (20 cm); 1 cm by 3 cm will have an area (3 cm²) less than the perimeter (8 cm)
4	Any 4 from: 1 and 60, 2 and 30, 3 and 20, 4 and 15, 5 and 12, 6 and 10 (all dimensions are in centimetres)
5	320 cm²

Area of Triangles (p.136)

Check-in

1	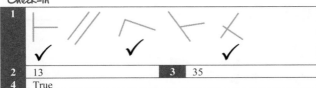

2	13	3	35
4	True		

Set?

A	(i)	6 cm²	C	(i)	24 m²
	(ii)	35 mm²		(ii)	20 cm²
	(iii)	54 m²			
B	(i)	15 cm²			
	(ii)	22 cm²			
	(iii)	30 m²			

Go!

1	For example:
	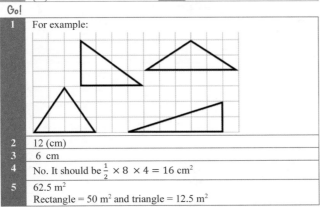
2	12 (cm)
3	6 cm
4	No. It should be $\frac{1}{2} \times 8 \times 4 = 16$ cm²
5	62.5 m²
	Rectangle = 50 m² and triangle = 12.5 m²

Area of Compound Shapes (p.138)

Check-in

1	False. The area is 24 cm²	
2	15 cm²	32 cm²
	15 cm²	6 cm²

Set?

A	(i)	44 cm²
	(ii)	78 cm²
	(iii)	30 m²
B	(i)	36 cm²
	(ii)	96 m²
	(iii)	47 cm²

Go!

1	23 cm²
2	10 cm
3	No, he has not split the shape. The correct answer is 37 cm²
4	The area of paint is 60 m², so 5 litres of paint are needed

Drawing Lines, Angles and Shapes (p.140)

Set?

A	(i)	A line of length 3 cm
	(ii)	A line of length 16 cm
	(iii)	A line of length 8.5 cm
	(iv)	A line of length 11.3 cm
B	(i)	An angle of 50°
	(ii)	An angle of 65°
	(iii)	An angle of 15°
	(iv)	An angle of 150°
	(v)	An angle of 165°
		See www.justaroo.co.uk/solutions for detailed solutions
C	(i)	Accurate drawing of the triangle
	(ii)	Answer between 7.4 and 7.8 cm
D		Accurate drawing of an isosceles triangle
		See www.justaroo.co.uk/solutions for detailed solutions

Go!

1	Accurate drawing of an equilateral triangle with side length 3 cm
	See www.justaroo.co.uk/solutions for detailed solutions
2	135° is obtuse and the angle he has drawn is acute
	He has used the wrong scale on the protractor
3	Accurate drawing of the shape
	See www.justaroo.co.uk/solutions for detailed solutions
4	Answer between 5.4 and 5.8 cm

Angles at a Point (p.142)

Check-in

1	4		
2	280		155
	200		150
	260		240
	80		55

Set?

A	(i)	260°	C	(i)	70°
	(ii)	155°		(ii)	210°
	(iii)	45°			
B	(i)	80°			
	(ii)	205°			
	(iii)	30°			

Go!

1	55°
2	The three missing angles are:
	120°, 30° and 40° or
	130°, 20° and 40° or
	140°, 20° and 30°
3	No, she has information about three angles as one of them is 90°
	The correct answer is x = 120°
4	60° (360° ÷ 6)

Angles at a Point on a Line (p.144)

Check-in

1	2		
2	70		140
	155		90
	130		135
	110		85

Set?

A	(i)	130°
	(ii)	135°
	(iii)	65°
B	(i)	120°
	(ii)	40°
	(iii)	80°
C	(i)	70°
	(ii)	25°

Go!

1	35°
2	47°, 23°, 65° and 45° or
	47°, 25°, 63° and 45° or
	67°, 25°, 43° and 45°
3	No, because the angles do not meet at a point on a line
4	No. For example: The angles could be 1°, 1°, 1°, 1° and 176°
	(176° is obtuse not acute)

Angles in a Triangle (p.146)

Check-in

1	Rings around: 100 150		
2	Ring around: Isosceles		
3	40	4	65

Set?

A	(i)	50°
	(ii)	45°
	(iii)	60°
B	(i)	60°
	(ii)	25°
	(iii)	35°
C	(i)	50°
	(ii)	75°
	(iii)	45°

Go!

1	The sum of angles in a triangle is 180°
	All three angles in an equilateral triangle are equal
	180 ÷ 3 = 60°
2	No, x and the unmarked angle are equal
	180 − 40 = 140 and 140 ÷ 2 = 70
	x = 70°
3	65°
4	The sum of two obtuse angles is always greater than 180°
	(Obtuse angles are between 90° and 180°)
5	a = 85°
	b = 150°

Coordinates 1 (p.148)

Check-in

1

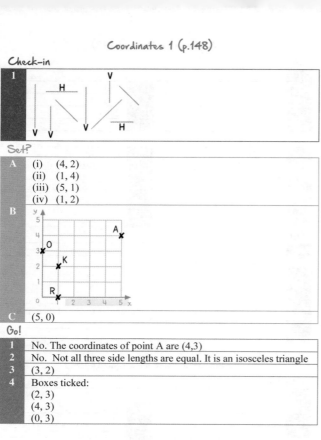

Set?

A
(i) (4, 2)
(ii) (1, 4)
(iii) (5, 1)
(iv) (1, 2)

B

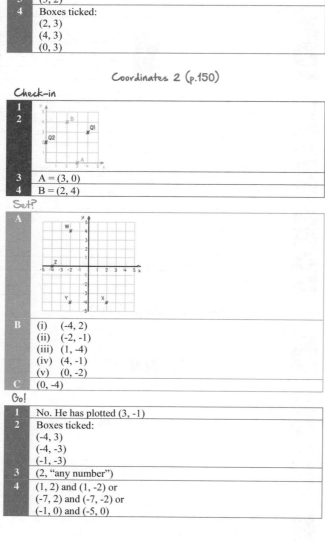

C (5, 0)

Go!

1 No. The coordinates of point A are (4,3)
2 No. Not all three side lengths are equal. It is an isosceles triangle
3 (3, 2)
4 Boxes ticked:
(2, 3)
(4, 3)
(0, 3)

Coordinates 2 (p.150)

Check-in

1
2

3 A = (3, 0)
4 B = (2, 4)

Set?

A

B
(i) (-4, 2)
(ii) (-2, -1)
(iii) (1, -4)
(iv) (4, -1)
(v) (0, -2)

C (0, -4)

Go!

1 No. He has plotted (3, -1)
2 Boxes ticked:
(-4, 3)
(-4, -3)
(-1, -3)
3 (2, "any number")
4 (1, 2) and (1, -2) or
(-7, 2) and (-7, -2) or
(-1, 0) and (-5, 0)

Reflections (p.152)

Check-in

1 A = (2, 1) B = (0, -1) C = (-2, 2)

Set?

A
(i)
(ii)
(iii)
(iv)

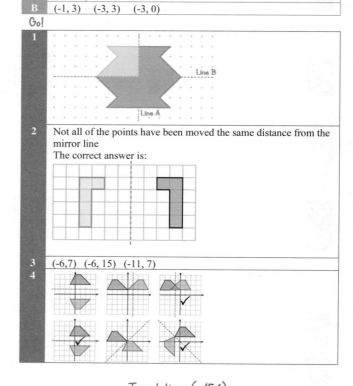

B (-1, 3) (-3, 3) (-3, 0)

Go!

1

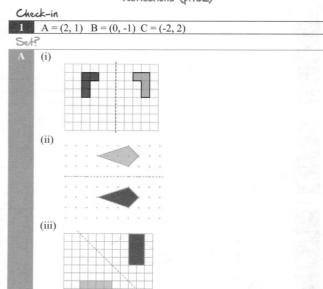

2 Not all of the points have been moved the same distance from the mirror line
The correct answer is:

3 (-6,7) (-6, 15) (-11, 7)
4

Translations (p.154)

Check-in

1

Left
Right
Up
Down

Set?

A

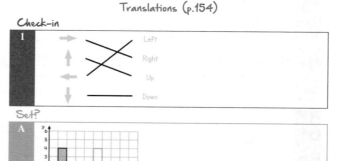

190

B	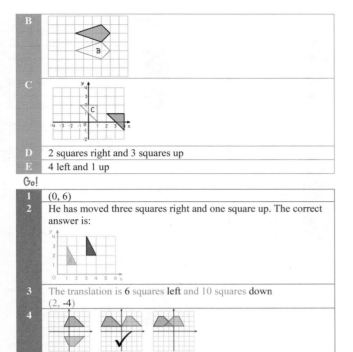
C	
D	2 squares right and 3 squares up
E	4 left and 1 up

Go!

1	(0, 6)
2	He has moved three squares right and one square up. The correct answer is:
3	The translation is 6 squares **left** and 10 squares **down** (2, -4)
4	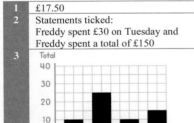

Tables and Charts (p.156)

Check-in

1	7
2	6
3	50

Set?

A	(i)	12
	(ii)	5
B	(i)	£20.50
	(ii)	£10.50
	(iii)	£1.50
C	(i)	5
	(ii)	Rock
	(iii)	5
	(iv)	50
D		

Sport	Total people
Tennis	6
Football	12
Rugby	14
Swimming	8

Go!

1	£17.50
2	Statements ticked: Freddy spent £30 on Tuesday and Freddy spent a total of £150
3	
4	All images ticked as they are all the same

Line Graphs (p.158)

Check-in

1	3, 14 and 48

Set?

A	(i)	6 mm
	(ii)	18 mm
	(iii)	28 mm

B	(i)	10 °C
	(ii)	6 °C
	(iii)	15:00
	(iv)	Between 13:00 and 14:00
C	(i)	12 km
	(ii)	45 minutes
D	(i)	13:30
	(ii)	-2 °C

Go!

1	The difference in temperature between 14:00 and 16:00 is 4°C The difference in temperature between 13:00 and 15:30 is 11°C
2	No. She has read the scale incorrectly. The correct distance was 4 km from home
3	(a) 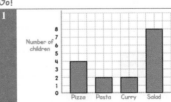 (b) 5:00 p.m. and 10:00 p.m.
4	21 °C

Pie Charts (p.160)

Check-in

1	25	2	50
3	6	4	120
5	8	6	15
7	False. The number equals 24 so $\frac{1}{8}$ of the number is 3		

Set?

A	(i)	$\frac{1}{2}$
	(ii)	25%
B	Statements ticked: 50% of the children chose dog The same number of children chose cat as fish 4 children chose cat Twice as many children chose dog than rabbit	
C	(i)	6
	(ii)	12
D		

Music	Number of people
Pop	10
Rock	15
Classical	10
Jazz	5

Go!

1	
2	

Subject	Number of people
Maths	12
English	6
History	6
Science	24

Number of people = 48

3	25 pupils is more than half of the class. The pie chart shows one quarter of the class have no pet.
4	For example:

The Mean (p.162)

Check-in

1	7		15
2	Ring around: 6.5		
3	Ring around: 2.5		

Set?

A	(i) 2	C	(i) 2.5
	(ii) 4		(ii) 5
	(iii) 2		(iii) 1.5
B	(i) 5	D	7 kg
	(ii) 5	E	3 km
	(iii) 2		

Go!

1	4 and 6
2	He should have divided by 5 as there are 5 numbers The correct answer is 4
3	3 mm
4	11 ($6 \times 12 = 72$, $72 + 5 = 77$ and $77 \div 7 = 11$)

Ratio and Proportion (p.164)

Check-in

1	120		60
	30		8
	0.8		2.4
2	Ring around: 3.5		

Set?

A

Number of red beads	Number of yellow beads	Total number of beads
15	3	18
25	5	30
40	8	48
50	10	60

B 40 (pens)

C 45 (scones)

D

Map distance	Real-life distance
3 cm	60 km
5 cm	100 km
1.5 cm	30 km
3.5 cm	70 km

Go!

1	200 (ml)
2	$5 \times 4 = 20$, so she needs to work out 2×4 (= 8) There will be 8 yellow beads
3	80p or £0.80
4	135 metres
5	A necklace has 4 beads for every 1 blue bead It has 52 red beads and 13 blue beads

Introduction to Algebra (p.166)

Check-in

1	16		
2	21		
3	5	4	10
5	6	6	7

Set?

A	(i) 4	C	(i) 8	E	
	(ii) 8		(ii) 10		
	(iii) -1		(iii) 6		
B	(i) 18	D	(i) 20		
	(ii) 12		(ii) 15		
	(iii) 32				

E

a	b
1	6
2	5
3	4
4	3
5	2
6	1

Go!

1	3 and 8
2	No. He needs to divide 28 by 2 The correct answer is $x = 14$
3	$\triangle = 7$ $\bigcirc = 9$
4	a = 4
5	a = 8 and b = 4

Formulae (p.168)

Check-in

1	42	2	80
3	200	4	150
5	300	6	24
7	6	8	8
9	70	10	7

Set?

A	£56	C	24 cm^2	E	8 (cakes)
B	54 cm^2	D	£50		

Go!

1	2:05 (p.m.)
2	7 (kg)
3	Ed's cost = $40 + 2 \times 50 = £140$ Beyonce's cost = $40 + 4 \times 50 = £240$ £240 is not double £140
4	$b = 10 \times a - 2$

Solving Word Problems (p.170)

Set?

A	1,207 points	D	40 balls
B	£7.25	E	125 sweets
C	15 cards	F	8 coaches

Go!

1	480
2	They have each bought 112 packets
3	219 (beads)
4	1,400 (leaflets)
5	80 (p)